Person-centred active support

A handbook

Bev Ashman,
John Ockenden,
Julie Beadle-Brown
and Jim Mansell

Person-centred Active Support:
a handbook

© Pavilion Publishing 2010

The authors have asserted their rights in accordance with the *Copyright, Designs and Patents Act 1988* to be identified as the authors of this work.

Published by:
Pavilion Publishing and Media Ltd
Rayford House
School Road
Hove
BN3 5HX
UK

Tel: 01273 43 49 43
Fax: 01273 62 55 56
Email: info@pavpub.com
Web: www.pavpub.com

First published 2010, reprinted 2012

A Catalogue reference for this book is available from the British Library.

ISBN: 978-1-84196-272-6

Pavilion is the leading publisher and provider of professional development products and services for workers in the health, social care, education and community safety sectors. We believe that everyone has the right to fulfil their potential and we strive to supply products and services that help raise standards, promote best practices and support continuing professional development.

Editor: Sanaz Nazemi, Pavilion
Cover design: Emma Garbutt, Pavilion
Page layout and typesetting: Emma Garbutt, Pavilion
Printed on paper from a sustainable resource by: IQ Laserpress

Person-centred active support

A handbook

Bev Ashman,
John Ockenden,
Julie Beadle-Brown
and Jim Mansell

Contents

Contents

Introduction

This handbook provides additional information on implementing person-centred active support developed as a result of our experience. It can be used to support the training pack *Person-centred Active Support: A multi-media pack for staff to enable participation, inclusion and choice for people with learning disabilities* (Mansell *et al*, 2005). However, it can also be read independently.

Our aim has been to write a book that is useful for practitioners who are planning to or are currently implementing person-centred active support. It is not intended to be a textbook or a precise guide to implementation, but reflects the fact that we have learned that different approaches, techniques and tools can help practice leaders and teams to develop systems and structures which meet their particular needs and those of the people they are supporting. We hope that providing examples, tools and experiences from our work in supporting better practice will help the reader to connect with the issues discussed and find it easier to relate them to their own experiences.

The language used to label and categorise people with learning disabilities changes over time and place. Throughout this handbook, we use the phrases 'learning disabilities' and 'people we support' because they are the choice of many self-advocates in the UK. The term 'learning disabilities' is comparable with the internationally accepted term 'intellectual disability', 'mental retardation' in the United States of America and 'mental handicap' in other countries. The term 'people we support' replaces terminology like 'service user' and 'client'.

The overall structure of the book takes the reader from historical background through practical experience, general principles, key elements and specific applications, to issues of team work, management and organisation.

Chapter 1, provides background information on active support, how and why it has developed to become person-centred active support and reiterates the importance of engagement and the need to focus on organising high-quality support. Chapter 2 recounts the experiences of organisations currently implementing person-centred active support and highlights a number of common themes and issues for consideration.

In Chapter 3, we outline the essential components of person-centred active support: 'every moment has potential', 'little and often', 'graded assistance' and 'choice and control' and the need for staff to develop a 24/7 approach. Following on from this, Chapter 4 explores the need to increase predictability and focuses on the development of effective, person-centred shift planning, and Chapter 5 provides information on a range of tools which can help teams to develop consistency of support across teams and within activities. Chapter 6 looks at the importance of team meetings and developing effective teamwork.

Practice leadership, an important component in the successful implementation of person-centred active support, is defined in Chapter 7, and we explore where responsibility for practice leadership lies and the obstacles to developing this role. The impact of skills and motivation on staff performance and how practice leaders can influence these factors is explored further in Chapter 8 and the effective use of modelling and coaching is covered in Chapter 9. The development of effective reviewing systems, which help teams to improve their practice, another important element of practice leadership and effective implementation, is discussed in Chapter 10.

Links between person-centred active support and other approaches to support, along with the importance of person-centred action are discussed in Chapter 11, which also considers the use of person-centred active support at home, work and in the community. Chapter 12 considers the issues of implementing person-centred active support with people with complex needs such as profound and multiple learning disabilities and autism spectrum disorders, and Chapter 13 investigates the interplay between person-centred active support and positive behaviour support when supporting people whose behaviour staff find challenging.

In recognition of the need to review and continue to develop person-centred active support, we have included information from providers on their approach to evaluation and the impact this has had on the development of person-centred active support in their organisation in Chapter 14. We also conclude with a summary of what our experience of implementing person-centred active support to date tells us and the key points for the future in Chapter 15.

Person-centred active support: A handbook

About the authors

Bev Ashman is practice development co-ordinator for United Response, a national organisation providing a range of services for people with learning disabilities, mental health needs or physical disabilities in England and Wales. She has been working with people with learning disabilities in New Zealand and the UK for more than 25 years and her interests include practice, service development, service systems and challenging behaviour. Bev has been working to assist United Response implement and evaluate person-centred active support nationally since 1998.

John Ockenden has worked with people with learning disabilities in a wide variety of roles and settings for 25 years. Since 2001, he has worked with United Response's practice development team advising support workers, managers and directors in the development of better practice and has a key role in the development of training materials and the practical application of person-centred active support, positive behaviour support, effective communication and person-centred approaches.

Julie Beadle-Brown has worked at the Tizard Centre, University of Kent, since 1995. Julie is senior lecturer in learning disabilities and primarily teaches on the postgraduate programmes in intellectual and developmental disabilities. Her research interests range from deinstitutionalisation and development of community-based services, service design and quality to personalisation, active support and quality of life for people with intellectual disabilities and children and adults with autism. She also spends a substantial amount of time working in services, training staff and evaluating service quality, with a particular focus on person-centred active support.

Jim Mansell is director of the Tizard Centre and professor of learning disability at the University of Kent, and an associate director of the NIHR School of Social Care Research. He is a fellow of the British Psychological Society and an Academician of the Social Sciences. He has been involved in the research and development of community-based learning disability services in England and Wales since 1970. He is a trustee of the charity United Response.

Acknowledgements

We would like to thank the staff and people we support from United Response who have provided stories and helped in the development of the materials. In particular, we would like to thank Bob Tindall and Bob Iles and members of the United Response Inclusion Team.

We would like to acknowledge our debt to the original training materials developed in the 1980s by our colleagues at the University of Kent (Hilary Brown and Sandy Toogood) and in the 1990s at the University of Cardiff (Edwin Jones, Jonathan Perry, Kathy Lowe, David Allen, Sandy Toogood and David Felce).

Thanks also go to Phoebe Caldwell and Sarah Broadhurst for spending time with us and helping us to understand how person-centred active support interlinks with other approaches to supporting people with complex needs.

Chapter 1

Background and importance of person-centred active support

'People with learning disabilities have the same rights as everyone else (United Nations, 1975). To have these rights in practice, people often need help. This help needs to be tailored to each person's individual situation. It needs to be person-centred.'

Mansell *et al*, 2005

The principles of normalisation (Nirje, 1969; Wolfensberger, 1972) promote the idea that people with learning disabilities should live in ordinary places, doing ordinary things, with ordinary people: essentially experiencing the 'normal' patterns of everyday life. Normalisation informed, and to some extent, drove the move away from institutional care towards community-based supports.

Wolfensberger (1983) later developed normalisation into the concept of 'social role valorisation' in order to suggest that particular attention should be paid to promoting valued social roles for people with disabilities, as a means of countering society's generally unhelpful attitudes to them. These principles were in turn used in the development of John O'Brien's (1987) *Five Accomplishments*, which have endured as a guiding framework in learning disability services today.

While there were reports of excellent outcomes for the people being supported in a number of demonstration projects in the early days of community care, concerns began to emerge that the inherent opportunities provided by community living were not, in reality, being fully utilised. It appeared that staff and managers were struggling to find ways to interpret the goals of normalisation when supporting people with substantial impairments.

Our discussions with staff over the years tell us that:

- it was common for principles of normalisation to be simplified into mantras about 'treating people normally'
- adapting activities and interactions was discouraged and fell out of use, as the approach was thought to be contrary to normalisation
- aids for activity and communication were removed or excluded from people's houses because of their disability associations – similarly staff were discouraged from using sign language [e.g. Makaton] in public
- talking to people 'normally' was viewed as the only acceptable means of interacting
- staff were encouraged only to see the positive attributes of people they supported, and to avoid referring to or dwelling upon their disability
- a normal physical environment and a valuing approach by a staff team were deemed sufficient ingredients to ensure a good quality of life for people
- staff did things for people in order to avoid doing them in ways that weren't 'normal'
- specific guidance about supporting people's challenging behaviour was not maintained or developed because it would promote a stigmatising attitude to the person. In its absence, but still needing to do something in often extreme circumstances, staff felt encouraged (or at least permitted) to respond to challenging behaviour using principles derived from childrearing, restitution and law enforcement
- induction training, beyond the legal minimum requirement, commonly focused largely on values
- many people, especially those with complex needs, had become observers of, rather than participants in, community life.

Observation

I recently visited a service to carry out an evaluation observation. The staff at the service were extremely busy throughout my two hour visit, rushing from one job to another, making drinks, getting dinner ready, doing laundry, clearing up after dinner and so on. Meanwhile the people they were supporting spent most of the time waiting in the lounge with the TV on in the background. Because the staff were busy, there was little social interaction. The only time this changed was during the meal when people were supported to eat their dinner.

Bev, practice development co-ordinator, United Response

It is not our intention to criticise the development and implementation of enlightened attitudes to people with a learning disability. Indeed these are at the heart of our work.

However, in this book we are addressing the need for integration and balancing of complementary perspectives and objectives. We write from the basic principle that we need to enable people with a learning disability to enjoy the same rights as all other citizens and we need to work carefully with them in a way that recognises their difficulties, impairments and disabilities. Through the best of intentions, the balance has frequently been tipped too far away from the latter to enable effective support and life enhancing outcomes.

Our work in community services in the UK, along with substantial numbers of research projects, has identified two major factors which directly impact on the engagement of people with learning disabilities.

1. The abilities of the person being supported; and

2. The quality and amount of 'assistance' (instructions, guidance, prompting) provided by the staff.

The quality of staff support, and the extent to which it provides precisely what is needed, is one of the most important factors influencing the quality of life of people with learning disabilities – especially for people with higher support needs. Research on the implementation of active support provides clear evidence that people can significantly increase the extent to which they participate in meaningful activities if staff adopt this approach.

Active support

By the early 1990s, a number of studies had shown that community-based services were not achieving the results indicated by the pilot projects on which they were based. They confirmed that, quite correctly, attention was going on buildings and location but that not nearly enough was being given to the quality of staff support for, and interaction with, the people being supported. A number of common problems, supporting the anecdotal information described above, were identified as follows.

Lack of planning and structure within services

Institutions were often barren, lacked meaningful activities and variety and this resulted in uninteresting and restrictive environments. For many people, living in this environment the routine and predictability of certain things e.g. meals, drinks, bath and bedtime, acted as markers for the day. These routines assisted these people to manage in the environment and make sense of their world.

One of the common results of moving into community services was that this routine and predictability was being removed, because of its institutional associations, and replaced by unexplained changes to these markers as well as increased pressure to choose or decide what would happen next. For a number of people with severe or profound disabilities, limited communication skills, autism or challenging behaviour, this made the world appear unpredictable, confusing and erratic.

Limited opportunities to participate in real activities

It was common, particularly in services for people with complex needs to find staff spending the majority of their time doing household tasks such as washing, ironing, polishing, hoovering, making beds and preparing drinks and meals, while the people being supported waited. By doing the 'natural' activities of living in the community for people, staff were limiting the opportunities for them to be engaged in meaningful activities and in associated interactions.

Low levels of contact with the people being supported

Despite the fact that the new community-based services had higher staffing ratios than the hospital wards they replaced, the anticipated increase in staff time spent engaging with and supporting people was often not being achieved in practice. Again there were a number of reasons for this, including the exclusion, by staff, of people from involvement in household tasks.

Staff training had become focused on values and statutory requirements

Recruitment information indicated that a high percentage of staff received little or no specific training in understanding and supporting people with learning disability. Induction and team training had become focused on values training and statutory requirements for training such as health and safety, food hygiene, first aid and lifting and handling.

At a meeting in London in the early 1990s, Jim Mansell, Eric Emerson and David Felce discussed these findings and agreed to promote the label 'active support' as a way of identifying the approaches needed to increase the effectiveness of staff support given to people with learning disabilities.

Active support is based on work originally carried out by Mansell *et al* (1983; 1987) in one of the first staffed houses for people with severe and profound learning disabilities in England.

Extract from Editorial – Tizard Learning Disability Review volume 3 (2)

The aim of 'active support' is to provide a good life for people with severe and profound learning disabilities by helping them directly engage in all the activities of daily life in the home and the community. This approach recognises that just providing a house in the community will not of itself be enough for people with major disabilities, and that without particularly skilled staff help there is a risk that institutional models of care will be recreated.

In general, 'active support' has four components, as follows.

■ **Real activities at home and in the community**
Service users are offered opportunities to take part in everyday activities at home and in the community, rather than childish or special therapeutic activities. The advantages of using real activities are (i) there is much more variety (ii) many service users find them more interesting (iii) they are less dependent on staff to signal every step and (iv) they provide opportunities for service users to show that they can take part successfully in ordinary activities like other people (Mansell *et al*, 1982; Felce *et al*, 1984).

■ **Staff organise the support they offer**
Staff pay particular attention to working as a team and to scheduling and co-ordinating the choices and opportunities they offer. This involves establishing routines (like those found in everyone's lives) for the carrying out of ordinary activities and regular planning (on a shift or daily basis) of how they will systematically share themselves across clients to provide the high level of support needed, often by more than one person at a time, for meaningful participation.

■ **Staff use an 'enabling' style of interaction**
Staff focus on helping service users take part minute-by-minute ('every moment has potential'), finding the parts of complicated tasks that even the most disabled person can do and doing the other parts of the task themselves, so that the person is almost guaranteed to succeed. Staff provide graded levels of assistance to ensure success and take account of individual preferences for activities and types of help to reduce the likelihood of challenging behaviour.

■ **Staff improve their practice**
Staff carefully monitor, using simple record keeping procedures, the degree to which service users are taking part in ordinary activities with the right level

and kind of support. Regular client-centred staff meetings allow plans to be modified in light of experience and support consistent practices across the staff group.

Extensive disengagement is taken to mean that staff are not offering sufficiently interesting opportunities, or that the way they are offering or supporting them is not sufficiently helpful and motivating, rather than that the service user is OK (Mansell, 1998).

From active support to person-centred active support

Active support developed into person-centred active support in 2004 in response to major developments that were taking place at the time, and following feedback from a range of individuals and organisations who were implementing the approach.

We were aware that the increasing emphasis on person-centredness made the earlier focus on the organisation of a group of staff supporting a group of people, less relevant and meant that some staff were finding it difficult to see how the approach should be implemented in supported living situations.

Our experience was that, too often, staff focused the implementation of active support on household activities and experienced difficulty generalising the information they were given to include actively supporting people in a range of community activities and relationships.

Reviewing the work done in some services also enabled us to see that a significant number of staff saw the primary focus of active support as the production of paper plans and record keeping.

As a result, we made changes to the overall messages and the staff training materials about person-centred active support so they would be useful to individuals as well as teams. We highlighted the connection between person-centred active support, as an example of person-centred action, and the development of person-centred planning, and we emphasised that person-centred active support is above all about engagement (minute-by-minute, day-by-day) and not about paperwork and plans.

Key principles of person-centred active support

Supporting engagement

'We know that activity is important for our physical and mental well-being. Lack of activity can lead both to physical health problems (such as obesity and heart disease) and to psychological problems (depression, boredom, lack of motivation, low self-esteem).'

(Mansell *et al*, 2005)

The primary aim of person-centred active support is to enable staff to support people to engage in meaningful activity and relationships because taking part in a range of activities provides experience of variety in life and the opportunity to make real and informed choices. Being actively involved increases the opportunities the people we support have to interact with others in meaningful and purposeful ways, on a more equal footing, rather than being the person that is 'spoken at' or 'done to'. It ensures that people with learning disabilities are seen by others as someone who is taking part and in control, thereby increasing their status and promoting opportunities to attract others into their lives.

Engagement is defined as:

- doing something constructive with materials (e.g. vacuum cleaning a floor, laying a table, cutting a hedge, loading a washing machine, listening to a radio)
- interacting with people (e.g. talking or listening to them or paying attention to what they do – holding a conversation, watching someone show how to do something)
- taking part in a group activity (e.g. watching the ball and running after it in football).

(Mansell *et al*, 2005)

Because many people with severe disabilities find it difficult to engage for long periods of time, we would not necessarily expect to see the same level of engagement for people with severe disabilities as their non-disabled peers. But our experience tells us that good support can significantly increase the extent to which people with severe and profound learning disabilities participate in meaningful activities.

With sufficient help, people can participate in all the opportunities that take place at home and in the community in different ways:

- doing the whole activity or interaction
- doing part of the activity or interaction

- being engaged continuously, throughout the activity or interaction
- dipping in and out of the activity or interaction
- taking the lead role in the activity or interaction
- joining in as an active participant.

Staff observation

Ian enjoys being in the kitchen while the meal is being prepared. For years he has sat at the breakfast bar watching staff prepare food on the kitchen counter. About six months ago, we reviewed this and agreed that we would move the preparation to the breakfast bar in front of Ian and support him to participate.

Since then we've changed the way we do some things (e.g. peeling the potatoes with a peeler and not a knife) and some of the equipment we use (e.g. an adapted chopping board that holds vegetables firmly for peeling and cutting).

He doesn't do the whole thing himself, mainly because he needs lots of physical support to get involved and he isn't used to doing things for a long time. He joins in for a couple of minutes then takes a break by sitting back. If you wait another minute or so and point back to the peeler, he'll usually join in again.

Ian loves it, now he sits at the breakfast bar waiting to get started on the evenings he's at home for dinner.

Janine, key worker, Blackpool

Person-centred active support is a way of providing the right kind and level of support. Too much, and the person being supported will not experience control of the activity or interaction; too little and there is a danger that they will experience failure. Implementation of person-centred active support requires staff to take account of the person's needs and preferences when developing their support strategies and recognising that these need to be used consistently by all members of the staff team.

The implementation of person-centred active support addresses the need to plan the use of time and resources to respond to the needs and wishes of the people being supported rather than staff preferences or service needs. It also recognises that for support to be person-centred, people's routines and rituals must be recognised and incorporated into the service and daily planning and structures.

Staff observation

While reviewing a support profile for Paul, it struck me that despite the fact that his ritual of checking all the windows and doors in the house before going out was recorded in the file, the additional time this requires whenever Paul goes out had not been incorporated into our daily planners.

I asked about this at the next team meeting and found that because some people knew Paul well, they always adjusted the day to ensure Paul had plenty of time to do this before going out. But others did not and were finding going out with Paul more and more difficult.

We agreed we needed to 'respect' Paul's going out ritual by doing more than writing it in his file: we actually needed to change the way we support him to incorporate this into the day.

Both the support plan and shift plans were changed as a result of this, but more importantly we changed what we actually do with Paul and he's much less stressed about going out as a result.

Sally, team member, Suffolk

Choice and control

Person-centred active support recognises that real choice requires experience – something which has often been unavailable to people with learning disabilities (particularly those with severe disabilities and complex needs).

Taking the view that extensive disengagement is not a real choice by the individual being supported, but is a failure of the service and the support being provided, person-centred active support refocuses staff on the broader goals of presence, competence, participation and respect and helps them to identify ways to widen people's experience and to give them more opportunities from which they can select.

It recognises that a balance between choice and responsibility is a reality for the people we support and that the goal of choice is not just about asking people whether or not they want to do something, but about respecting people's decisions in a range of situations including where and when things happen, how they unfold and how they are paced.

A key strength in person-centred active support is the recognition that real choice and control for people with severe disabilities and complex needs will require staff to have a clear understanding of rejection and the ability to utilise feedback from the person they are supporting to make a 'best guess' about what to try in the future.

Staff observation

The people we support here have profound learning and physical disabilities and have lived in institutions for most of their lives. In the past, we have found it really difficult to develop person-centred plans for people, which go beyond ensuring people are healthy and safe because people only communicate through their emotions and body language about the things that are going on immediately around them. While we had ideas about activities that an individual might like, the fact that we couldn't say for sure that this was what they wanted meant that we didn't feel it was right to support the individual to do them – we were stuck.

After discussing this at a team meeting, we agreed that in order to continue to improve the support and opportunities we provide, we needed to take our best guess so that people could experience new things and we could learn from their responses if we had got it right.

Since then we have been able to introduce people to lots of new activities and experiences. Sometimes our best guess is spot on and people love it. Sometimes we get it wrong and people don't enjoy things as much but that's OK too because it helps to build up our knowledge to make a better guess next time.

Cyndy, service manager, Manchester

Organising and improving practice

High-quality services and person-centred support cannot be achieved in services for people with learning disabilities without good organisation, planning and strong leadership. Person-centred active support suggests that practice leaders need to plan the limited resources available effectively to ensure staff are focused on supporting people to be actively engaged in a range of activities and relationships at home and in the community.

Person-centred active support recognises the importance of staff skills and motivation. It helps practice leaders clarify expectations and ensure staff are clear about their roles and responsibilities, enabling the team to help each other to improve the quality of their support.

Observation

I can remember a conversation with Jim Mansell when we first started implementing active support in a residential service in York in 1998. He used the example of a watch to explain the need to organise ourselves in such a detailed and specific way.

'What you are creating is a very ordinary looking thing – "an ordinary life", it's a typical day made up of a range of activities and relationships at home and in the community, that from the outside looks the same as other people's.'

Like the face on your watch – it's something you see everyday. But in order to create that everyday object, there are wheels, springs and gears working together in very accurate ways to make the watch function effectively.

Bev, practice development co-ordinator, United Response

Evidence of the outcomes of person-centred active support

The extent to which people with learning disabilities have been enabled to participate in meaningful activity in their homes and in the community has been the focus of attention for researchers for a long time and as a result, engagement and active support are among the best researched issues in services today and shows a consistent picture of benefits for people when staff adopt this model (Stancliffe *et al*, 2008; Totsika *et al*, 2008).

The framework in **figure 1** shows the inputs and outcomes identified by researchers, staff in services and the people they support.

Figure 1: Inputs and outcomes for person-centred active support

Person-centred active support inputs:	Outcomes:
Focus on engagement in meaningful activity and relationships	Increased engagement in meaningful activities and relationships
Graded assistance matched to individual needs and preferences	Increased levels and quality of support provided by staff
Effective support of choice and control	Increased skills and confidence of the people we support and staff
Planned use of time and resources	Enhanced person-centred planning and information about the people being supported
Person-centred daily planning	
Practice leadership	
Coaching and modelling of good practice	Effective person-centred team work, which is focused on practice development
Effective team work	
Increased staff skills and confidence	

Summary

The over-simplification of the principles of normalisation underpinning learning disabilities services has led to low levels of participation, particularly for people with severe and profound disabilities and a devaluing of important support practices may still be seen in many services today. Person-centred active support is an effective approach to counteracting this problem, increasing levels of engagement for people with learning disabilities and their quality of life.

Chapter 2

Providers' experiences of implementing person-centred active support

'Senior managers have a special responsibility to create a climate in which staff know that the most important part of their job is providing person-centred active support, in order to help people engage in meaningful activity and relationships.'

(Mansell *et al*, 2005)

This chapter contains information about implementation and lessons learnt from the implementation of person-centred active support from five organisations working directly with people with learning disabilities. While these organisations are different in size and from different parts of the world, their accounts demonstrate how person-centred active support can be implemented and identify common themes. We approached key people in each organisation and asked them to provide information on the following questions.

- Why did you decide to implement person-centred active support in your organisation?
- What concerns did you have prior to implementation?
- How did you implement person-centred active support?
- What difficulties have you encountered?
- What impact has it had?

1. Avenues Trust, Sidcup, England

Jayne Kilgallen

Why did you decide to implement person-centred active support in your organisation?

Avenues Trust was very proud of its many elements of service delivery and could describe the positive changes to the lives of people being supported. However, this was often sporadic and ad-hoc, and very much relied on staff to initiate and tell the stories.

We were also concerned that whilst people we support were getting out and about and being involved in some activities inside the house, many people spent long periods of time waiting for the next activity, whilst staff got on with household tasks in order to be ready to support people to go out or carry out hobbies at home, or simply be with each other.

Many of the people supported by Avenues have very complex and multiple needs and it was clear that staff were unsure as to how and what activities individuals could be involved in. There were also high levels of ritualistic and repetitive challenging behaviour exhibited.

Initially, Avenues had worked with the Tizard Centre to train staff to use the active support model, linking this with a number of key systems and structures in our east Kent services. The results of this work were extremely encouraging and further work was carried out across the remaining services in two years.

Having seen the success in east Kent, we were keen to ensure everyone who used Avenues services could benefit from person-centred active support.

This, together with an increasing push from commissioners and our own trustees, to demonstrate real outcomes for the people we support led to a decision in 2006 to fully implement person-centred active support across all of Avenues' services for people with a learning disability.

What concerns did you have prior to implementation?

Our concerns prior to implementation related to the robustness of services and our ability to maintain and develop person-centred active support after the initial training implementation. We were also worried that routine or critical operational matters may get in the way of successful implementation.

The model of person-centred active support requires the buy-in and participation of middle and frontline managers, and it was important to us that we recognised this and gave them the skills in the implementation phase. We therefore did three important things that we believe enabled the implementation to be successful.

Firstly, we allocated specific resources and appointed a co-ordinator who was managed outside of the operational management structure. We also gave a clear message to all staff across Avenues that this was the way we delivered services, and that there was 'no escape'. Finally, we developed a number of reporting systems that informed all levels of the organisation, including trustees, on progress at an individual service level.

How did you implement person-centred active support?

Avenues involved the Tizard Centre in supporting them to design an implementation plan over five years, train their senior managers as person-centred active support trainers and train the first six services. Avenues also recruited a person-centred active support co-ordinator to co-ordinate the implementation of active support across Avenues. The co-ordinator advises on best practice, helping to problem-solve when difficulties arise. They have trained Avenues' managers in conjunction with the Tizard Centre, and continue to support and develop them in their role as active support trainers, working with them to deliver training to staff teams.

Six services were chosen to pilot the training during 2006–07. Before training began, the Tizard Centre carried out observations in pilot services to establish baseline data on engagement levels and the quality of the staff support. They used questionnaires to establish the characteristics of the people we support, their participation in daily life, community involvement and choice-making. Each house manager was also interviewed about the service setting, homeliness, the systems and structures in place to support the involvement and activity of those supported, and staff training and monitoring. Staff teams were given confidential questionnaires to check the characteristics of staff, the training they had received, and their views on their experience at work, including job satisfaction, their experience of management and of teamwork and whether they received practice leadership. This helped establish what existing skills managers had and what further support they would need in their crucial role as practice leaders. Following this, training was delivered to the first six services, consisting of a one-day workshop on person-centred active support followed by two days on-the-job training and coaching, delivered by the Tizard Centre and the person-centred active support co-ordinator.

All operational senior managers in the organisation were trained as trainers in person-centred active support including the director of operations, all regional and service managers and some house managers. Additionally, the board of trustees were briefed on the model and they endorsed person-centred active support as a key part of the business plan. This has helped to ensure that staff have support from all levels of the organisation and that everyone remains focused on what is most important, i.e. the quality of life of those supported by Avenues.

A year after the training in the first six services, the Tizard Centre returned to evaluate the impact training had had on the quality of life of the people supported by Avenues and the quality of support provided by its staff. The results showed vast improvements in all areas and a significant decrease in challenging behaviour, which helped motivate everyone to achieve this across the board.

The training was then rolled out to the remaining 36 residential services over three years. All residential staff have now been trained and the roll-out has begun in Avenues' supported living subsidiary. The principles of person-centred active support have been incorporated into all staff training, including induction, person-centred planning, positive behaviour support, coaching, supervision and shift planning, with systems in place to train all new staff as part of their induction as soon as possible after their start date. It has also been incorporated into people's job descriptions and our rigorous quality assurance processes have been reviewed to reflect the importance of active support.

In addition, paperwork was reviewed and adapted in all services to ensure that recording was simple yet meaningful so that staff were not spending a great deal of time on administration at the expense of spending time with the people they support, but that important information was recorded and collated meaningfully for the people supported. As all senior managers, including corporate managers, have been trained, there is a shared understanding throughout Avenues of what we are striving to achieve for the people we support and their support staff.

What difficulties have you encountered?

Training
Following the training in the pilot services, Avenues reviewed how it was delivered. A cross-section of people involved in the training reviewed the training materials and how it was delivered. Feedback was sought from all those who had been trained and the training materials and format was consequently adapted to better suit Avenues staff. This included making the workshop more interactive and suited to different styles of learning and delivering the on-the-job coaching over three to four half days as opposed to two full days so as not to overload staff and the people we support.

Practice leadership
Research shows that the quality of staff support (leading to an increase in engagement) is strongly related to whether or not frontline managers provide strong practice leadership. Regular observation and modelling of good support to staff by managers,

combined with a focus on engagement and active support in team meetings and supervisions is very important. With this in mind, Avenues has been developing managers and seniors within services as practice leaders, supporting them to move away from a focus on administration and managing people to spend time leading by example, directly supporting service users, demonstrating good practice and coaching and giving constructive feedback to their staff. During the on-the-job coaching, each house manager, deputy and senior was trained in how to carry out observations, model good practice and provide positive, informative and motivating feedback to their staff. Avenues also developed learning and development opportunities to compliment this, such as its management courses and coaching for performance courses along with, for example, a revision of its effective supervision courses.

Consistency of approaches

Avenues recognised that implementing person-centred active support was not enough to improve the quality of staff support and the quality of services provided to the people it supports. More work was needed to be done to ensure that all person-centred approaches were employed together around each person supported. Avenues already had effective systems in place for person-centred planning and positive behaviour support but they were not always sufficiently complimented by total communication and positive approaches to autism and mental health issues. We have reviewed and adapted our training in these approaches and are always looking for ways to improve how this is delivered, for example, training teams together in all approaches so that the training can be tailored to the individual needs of those supported, and individual staff's learning and application in their workplace can be monitored. We have found team training to be much more effective than individual staff members attending training at different times. In addition, we have found that it is vital to ensure that all training delivered, whether internally or externally, gives staff the same clear message. For example, health and safety and food hygiene courses need to give staff the message that their job is to effectively manage risks and not avoid supporting people to take them.

Keeping the momentum going

One difficulty with implementing active support is that the enthusiasm and momentum seen at the outset may not be maintained long term. We have been very clear that training is only the beginning and that services should strive for continuous improvement and development, always looking for new opportunities for people to engage in. Support is available from all levels of the organisation and service managers, through their six-monthly observations they will clearly see whether the service is developing or whether they need support to do so. Every opportunity to celebrate individual staff and service user achievements should also be taken to boost morale and job satisfaction.

What impact has it had?

The implementation of active support across the organisation has had a huge impact on staff and those we support. The results across the first 26 services trained show that engagement in meaningful activity and relationships increased by 75%, assistance provided by staff increased by 233%, the quality of staff support increased by 49% and repetitive and self-stimulatory behaviour decreased by 26%.

However, as we are talking about people's quality of life, one of the most important ways of seeing the impact of person-centred active support is through anecdotal evidence and through telling people's stories. We have seen huge changes in individuals' lives from people getting jobs to people re-establishing contact with families to people becoming so much more assertive in making choices. Stories have been published in the staff and service user newsletter highlighting successes and staff that have been nominated for awards where active support has led to a particular success.

Cymryd Rhan, Llandrindod Wells, Wales

Jane Edwards

We have been developing our services to be increasingly person centred, supporting individuals to take more control over their lives and participate actively in their homes and communities. Developing our services to be person centred has meant examining the way we support people and using a variety of tools and approaches to support a process of staff training and development. Developing a person-centred culture is a whole organisation process, our admin and finance staff need to understand how we work and support staff teams to implement person-centred approaches as much as our frontline support workers need to change the way they work. Developing a coaching and mentoring approach to staff development across the organisation reinforces the view that we all have skills and abilities if we are given the chance to develop and use them.

Changing culture is a long, challenging, demanding and sometimes demoralising process. Some learning that assisted in this process came from the two day training event to launch the person-centred active support training pack. A couple of nuggets of wisdom, gleaned from the two days are, 'you need to repeat your message over and over again', staff don't always take in ideas the first time you present them, don't think because you have said it once people will understand and change their behaviour, you need to say it again and again and keep reinforcing the message and 'If you give your employees the message that being good at paperwork is what is important to this company then they will concentrate on the paperwork'.

Person-centred active support has been a crucial element of developing increasingly person-centred services. Cymryd Rhan has been implementing person-centred active support across the organisation over the past four years. We began with some training and consultancy from Julie Beadle-Brown from the Tizard Centre to train all of our frontline managers to be able to implement and train staff.

The managers having the skills to constantly reinforce good practice and coach and develop staff to use person-centred active support was key to ensuring that it became firmly embedded in the culture. Our experience is that if you just send staff on a training course they are unlikely to sustain a change in the way they work. The principles behind person-centred active support, of people becoming increasingly engaged in their daily lives and their communities help our staff to work in more person-centred ways. Once support workers have the skills to support people to do as much as they can for themselves then they can begin to get clear their role of supporting somebody to live their own life in their own home. It is very easy for support workers to take over people's lives and homes and for customs and practices to develop that are more about staff having rotas and practices that suit them, albeit often in very well meaning ways. Person-centred active support very much supports that change of culture we needed to make, from doing for people to doing with them and supporting them to increase their skills and take more control of their lives and homes.

One of the tremendous benefits we have seen from our use of person-centred active support is people gaining skills and confidence to move from shared supported living environments into their own homes, needing less support and doing much more for themselves. However, it also has a tremendous impact on the people we support with higher support needs increasing their engagement in activities and improving their quality of life and promoting their participation in their communities.

We have found that person-centred active support works well with other person-centred tools such as the person-centred thinking tools, as introduced by Helen Sanderson Associates. Person-centred active support can be implemented without lots of paperwork and it is much more about getting on and doing things, trying things out to find out what works and definitely not just doing paperwork. Good person-centred support plans describe how people prefer to be engaged and participate.

Our experience has been of person-centred active support contributing positively to a whole culture change.

Dimensions, Theale, England

Paul Pargeter

Why did you decide to implement person-centred active support in your organisation?

We believe that the single most effective way to help a person who requires a lot of support to experience a full and rich life is to ensure that they have every opportunity to be as engaged as possible in the things that go on in the real world. We provide support to a number of people who need skilled and mindful support workers to help them in life and – if implemented well – person-centred active support provides the principles, skills and techniques to maximise the chances of this happening.

We foresaw benefits for the people we support as well as their support teams, with the knowledge that if you are proud of your work and making a positive difference then morale and confidence are likely to increase. The measuring of person-centred active support and engagement was also a big incentive to Dimensions, as we are keen both to show the evidence of the benefits and keep track of areas that still need to improve. Accurate information from observations will help us perform our mantra which is: supporting people with learning disabilities and autism to live the life they want.

What concerns did you have prior to implementation?

Our concerns rest mainly with making sure the learning has a direct and positive impact on people. We wanted this practice to make as direct a leap as possible from the classroom to people's real lives. The development of person-centred active support (or most things for that matter) is reliant on sound implementation with a well thought through plan that not only helps kick off with some good results, but helps it enroot and thrive.

Another concern was that the presentation of person-centred active support would be too academic or inaccessible, leaving it too aloof for people to feel the passion to reach out and use it. People working for our organisation hear of many initiatives and programmes and it was vital to make this as real and useful as possible – the hands-on workshops have helped with this immensely.

How did you implement person-centred active support?

We are still in the process of implementing. Dimensions, is now a large and spread-out organisation so implementation has required some careful thought, and it's not been without its headaches. The fundamental plan has been to train-up local leads (those who have a capacity to do) who then work with their regional director to develop a local plan that works for the region (see **figure 1**). All plans have to include these non-negotiable elements as follows.

1. The objectives of the plan
2. Priorities in the region (including organisational priorities of registered care homes first and group living services second)
3. Timescales of the training plan
4. Inclusion of classroom-based workshops and hands-on workshops
5. How the region develops its expertise and capacity to train teams
6. System changes that compliment the shift towards active support (team meetings, supervisions, rota writing, management audits, practice leadership, on shift observations and feedback)
7. What success will look like
8. The monitoring of progress
9. All support teams trained by March 2012

The process

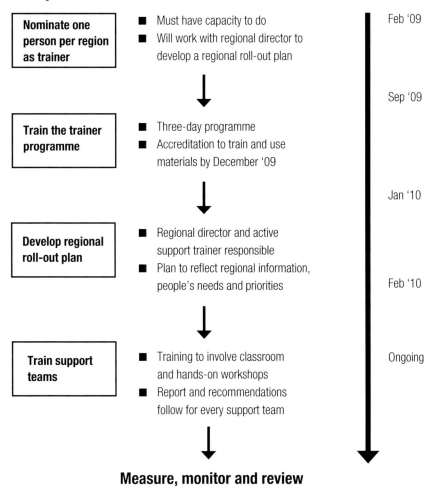

Figure 1: Dimensions active support strategy

What difficulties have you encountered?

Some regions have found capacity and have been really organised in getting on with implementation. Others have found it difficult to 'free-up' someone in order for them to lead on and develop person-centred active support in their region. Also, some people who have been through the train the trainer course have left the organisation. We are about to organise another round of training for regional leads to try and keep up the momentum.

It has been very clear that where leaders in a region are committed and organised, positive outcomes ensue.

What impact has it had?

Where implemented and practiced, the impact has been very positive. The impact occurs in different areas as follows.

The person

We have found that people we support have gained a lot in terms of their active participation and all-round experience in life. With some time and thought in almost all areas, we have seen people enjoy and benefit from person-centred active support. This has been particularly (though not exclusively) useful for people who have quite severe intellectual and physical disabilities.

The support worker and support team

For those that are keen to carry out person-centred principles at work, person-centred active support has provided a sense of pride and assurance. The benefits are welcomed, and in turn the sense of purpose has been a useful side effect to increase team morale and motivation. Of course, for some team members who do not wish to change in practice, it has been so conspicuous that it may have left them feeling rather alone and fearful, we expect this and encourage people to develop with us and not to stand still.

Leadership

We are just beginning to see the benefits of practice leadership. Anecdotal evidence leads us to believe that positive leadership and direction can make all the difference.

Systems

Some paperwork systems have been altered to become more in tune with person-centred active support, along with the way team meetings are conducted and the regular practice of observation and feedback in services.

Wider organisation

We have included some members of our learning and development team in the training programme so there is an appreciated link between person-centred active support and everything else we do.

Jewish Care, Victoria, Australia

Daniel Leighton

Why did you decide to implement person-centred active support in your organisation?

There were four main reasons for the decision to implement active support in Jewish Care.

1. We wanted to achieve a cultural change within the organisation and this required showing staff that there is a new or different way of doing things.
2. We wanted to achieve greater outcomes for residents.
3. We wanted to utilise training as a chance to build team unity and a sense of purpose.
4. We wanted to use implementation as a vehicle for review of staffing rosters – moving away from rosters designed around staff (e.g. family/personal needs) to matching client needs and interests.

What concerns did you have prior to implementation?

- Actually, once we had secured resources and funding, we had no concerns.

How did you implement person-centred active support?

- Implementation at Jewish Care was one of the first in Australia so there were few options – we contracted CDS (University of Sydney) to conduct three-day workshops with each house staffing team. There was an initial two-day programme, followed by one-day interactive training (one on one) in each house, followed by a follow-up session approximately three weeks later for a half day (this took place during the training for the next group).
- At the same time, staffing rosters were reviewed and amended, paperwork systems (household recording, diaries, etc.) reviewed to create a single standard reporting system utilising information collected through person-centred active support data capture where possible.

What difficulties have you encountered?

There have been three main issues encountered as follows.

1. Staff attitudes can be difficult to change. It is particularly difficult to change people from being carers to being enablers.
2. Sustaining person-centred active support over time can be very difficult.
3. It has also been quite difficult to find meaningful ways to measure the outcomes and build the evidence base for person-centred active support.

What impact has it had?

Despite the difficulties, there has been clear evidence that active support has been beneficial. In particular, we have seen:

- increased engagement in day-to-day activities
- more opportunities for greater engagement with families (i.e. demonstrating to parents what a person can do with the right amount of support).

United Response, London, England

Bob Tindall

Why did you decide to implement person-centred active support in your organisation?

The active support approach was initially developed as a response to the needs of people who challenge and the staff that support them in the north east of England. The implementation of active support in one of our services in York was significant in paving the way for the development of active support across United Response. This model of successful good practice was recognised as a way of working to increase the effectiveness of staff support by organising and tailoring it to individual needs.

In 1998, United Response introduced active support as an organisation-wide approach and was the first time the approach had been adopted by a national organisation across a wide range of geographically dispersed settings. As well as providing active-support training, we identified the implementation of active support as a corporate objective, developed organisational standards and carried out a review of organisational systems and structures.

What concerns did you have prior to implementation?

We knew that the development of active support had considerable organisational implications which needed to be addressed if it was to proceed effectively. We were aware that we could not assume that small changes here and there would be enough to ensure successful implementation of active support and needed to make staff aware that it is about continuous improvement, not a quick fix.

How did you implement person-centred active support?

In order to introduce active support and kick start the implementation process, we:

- integrated active support into organisational policies and standards, strategic plans, and staff-related procedures such as supervision and personal development planning
- continued to utilise external expertise from the Tizard Centre, which had supported us in the work in York

■ developed internal expertise by inviting service and area managers from across the organisation to become part of a focus group which met with our external experts – to develop confidence and expertise in the implementation of active support as well as to create real examples of active support in practice

■ created a steering group who were given the task of co-ordinating all aspects of the development of active support and ensuring that progress was being made

■ introduced mandatory active support training into the organisation's management training programme

■ appointed a dedicated internal person who could develop expertise and devote herself solely to the internal development of active support.

Since then we have continued to adapt our training and resources to match the changing organisational 'landscape' and to meet the wishes and needs of the people we are set up to support. The numerous changes and adaptations made over the last 12 years are too long to list here, but those that have had the biggest impact include the following.

■ The development of a practice development team and the introduction of practice 'surgeries' (bi-monthly meetings with area and service managers) which focus on planning, monitoring and supporting the implementation of practice plans.

■ The development to The Way We Work Framework (see **figure 2**) to help staff see how active support, communication, person-centred planning and other tools work together to develop an integrated person-centred approach for the people we support.

Figure 2: United Response, The Way We Work Framework

■ The introduction and adaptation of an evaluation process, which is accessible and meaningful to staff teams, ensures feedback, celebrates success and identifies actions to continue to develop person-centred active support.

What difficulties have you encountered?

As the first organisation to implement active support as an organisation-wide approach, there has been a lot of learning which has been shared widely and informed the development of the person-centred active support training materials written by Mansell *et al* in 2005.

Difficulties which continue to impact successful implementation include the following.

Maintaining momentum

As person-centred active support is a process of continual improvement and developing it can be difficult to maintain staff's enthusiasm in the long-term, changes to management structure and personnel, which reduce practice leadership and crises in services, can have a significant impact on the implementation of person-centred active support; and this can be difficult to correct.

New (external and internal) incentives, while important and valuable, can have the effect of refocusing staff's attention on the development of 'the new' which can result in significant decreases in effective person-centred support for individuals.

Generalising use of support skills

Staff can become focused on using person-centred active support during planned activities, but not fully utilising incidental opportunities to support people to participate. It is still difficult for some staff to see how they can use the skills they have developed to both support people successfully to participate in activities within the home and to enable people to be supported to develop community activities and relationships.

Practice leadership

The importance of practice leadership is recognised in the organisation and is reflected in management structures and job descriptions, but for a variety of reasons, some managers find it difficult to develop this role.

What impact has it had?

The implementation of active support has enabled staff to see how the organisational aim to provide high-quality person-centred support for all the people we support can really happen. Staff have become more skilled at working with people in an enabling way, supporting them to participate in a range of activities and relationships at home and in the community and to have more choice and control in their daily lives.

It has changed the way the organisation views and monitors success to focus on real outcomes for those being supported and helped us to remain grounded in doing things in a person-centred way. The development of The Way We Work Framework has enabled us to introduce new developments and new ways of working, including person-centred thinking and positive behaviour support, in a manner which integrates these approaches. This has enabled us to continue to improve the service provided and the support people receive rather than detract from it.

Over the last 12 years, the emphasis on practice development and practice leadership has helped us to ensure that managers focus on the minute-by-minute, day-to-day involvement of the people we support as the main priority.

Summary

While all five organisations have approached the implementation of person-centred approach differently, much of this work has focused on developing a clear and consistent message about the importance of person-centred active support in the organisation; involving senior management in the change process; developing practice leadership skills in coaching, observation and feedback, as well as training for all staff (including senior managers).

All organisations have reported increased engagement in meaningful activities and relationships which have improved the quality of life of the people they support. Increases in staff skills are also commonly reported and various organisational changes were also noted.

Keeping the momentum to implement and continue to develop person-centred active support is an issue for all five organisations and the development of effective practice leadership has been an issue for many.

Chapter 3

Essentials of person-centred active support

> '… with sufficient help, people can participate in all the opportunities for activities and relationships that take place at home and in the community throughout the day. Everyone can contribute, at least to some extent, even if they don't have all the skills needed; and everyone can choose preferred activities and increase their control over their environment.'
>
> Mansell *et al*, 2005

Successful implementation of person-centred active support requires staff to think about activities differently. Instead of thinking about activities and interactions as a whole, staff need to be able to identify the steps within them so they can recognise the parts that the people they are supporting can do themselves, the parts they can support people to do and the parts they need to do themselves in order to ensure the activity or interaction happens successfully. Staff need to provide the right type and level of support consistently so that the person they are supporting can participate in a wide range of activities and relationships successfully. This needs to become the way staff work throughout the day, rather than just in planned activities.

The essential components of active support enable staff to do this and can be summed up by these four headings as follows.

Every moment has potential

Staff need to look for opportunities to support people to participate in meaningful activities and interactions throughout the day. This means staff are constantly thinking about activities that need to be done (e.g. shopping, housework and gardening) and activities that are available to do (e.g. visit friends, play sports) and identifying the parts of activities and interactions that people can do, and then fill in the gaps by providing whatever support is needed.

This way of thinking is used in the first two sections of the 'improving your support skills' worksheet, which is included in the *Person-centred Active Support: A multi-media training pack* (see **table 1**). While this is a written document, the most effective staff learn to think through this process as they go, rather than having to rely on pre-planned instructions.

Table 1: Extract from 'Improving your support skills' worksheet (Mansell *et al*, 2005)			
1. Select a person you support and an activity or interaction.			
2. Identify the steps of the activity or interaction the person can do on their own, those they can do with some help, and the parts you will fill in for them.			
Steps that make up the activity or interaction	On own	With help	Staff to do

Little and often

A key principle of person-centred active support is helping people to engage 'little and often' so that they build up experience of success and enjoyment, and increase their motivation.

Mansell *et al*, 2005

Achieving this means staff need to make and take the time to do things with people – very often it is quicker and easier for staff to do things for people, but rushing to get things done results in the people we support missing a large percentage of the natural opportunities available to them to take part in their own lives (the organising and maintenance of their home, social life and role as active member of the community), missing opportunities to engage with the people around them and increasing the likelihood of the individual being seen as unskilled.

More often than not, it takes longer to do things in ways that involve people to the greatest extent and as a result staff teams may have to change their expectations about when and how things should be done and organise their time differently.

Staff observation

When I first started working here, there was an expectation that all the housework and recording would be done before the handover at 2pm. The first priority in the morning was to get people up and ready to go to the day centre, if they were going that day, which was fine, but then most of the remainder of the shift was spent making the beds, doing the laundry, mopping floors, vacuuming, dusting, ironing and cleaning. The people left at home ended up sitting in front of the TV all morning while we got on it. If we were really quick, we could fit in a cup of tea and a chat with people before we had to make lunch, then by the time you cleaned up the lunch dishes and helped people with personal care, you just had time to write up the shift notes and do the petty cash checks before the next shift arrived at 2pm.

While this meant that there was time to do community activities with the people we support between 2pm and 4pm (whatever was happening, staff had to be back before 4pm when the day centre transport arrived), I didn't like the fact that the people living here were left with nothing to do all morning.

After the active support training, we realised that we were denying the people we support the opportunity to take an active part in the running of their own house and started to involve people in the things that needed doing. We soon realised that involving people meant everything took longer and that it was no longer possible to get it all done before 2pm.

In order to make it work, we had to spread the housework through the day and week. OK, the vacuuming isn't done every day, sometimes the laundry and ironing piles up and when you come on shift in the afternoon the house is not immaculate, but it's still tidier than mine on most days when I'm at work. Now the people we support get involved in all the household activities, even if it's only parts of the job, and they love it! What's really interesting is that because we're planning the day better, and thinking more about how to involve people in everything that's happening, the community activities are also better planned which means people get out and about more than they were before.

Jenny, team member, Suffolk

'People who have very high support needs because of profound and multiple intellectual disabilities may only be able to sustain their involvement for a few seconds longer. Similarly, people with high support needs because of challenging behaviour might find new activities too much to take for more than a few minutes.'

Mansell *et al*, 2005

Many of the people we support are unable to sustain their involvement for long periods of time and as a result staff need to have a realistic starting point. 'Little and often' will mean different things for different people. For some people, it's joining in for five minutes – for others it's a few seconds. Staff teams need to identify people's current involvement preferences and then work consistently to involve people in the whole or part of activities and interactions, on a continuous or a stop–start basis.

Staff observation

A while ago we decided to involve Mark in vacuuming the lounge on Thursday and Monday afternoons. He'd never done it before but seemed to enjoy the sound of the vacuum cleaner and usually sat on the sofa watching the staff do it, with a big smile on his face.

After a couple of weeks, we were all feeling very disheartened about the idea, as Mark would come over and touch the vacuum cleaner while we were vacuuming, but he wouldn't hold onto it for more than a few seconds. He would do this three or four times and it became clear that he won't be doing the lounge on his own anytime soon.

We discussed our progress during the next team meeting and our manager pointed out that we were expecting too much from Mark. She told us that by Mark touching the vacuum cleaner three to four times for a few seconds, was Mark being involved 'little and often' and that this was a real success. We talked about how we could build on this by increasing the number of times Mark came over and touched the vacuum and also by supporting him to touch the vacuum for longer. Then we discussed how we could push the vacuum backwards and forwards while he was touching it – to make it more like the real thing.

Vacuuming (not just the lounge) is now one of Mark's favourite activities. When you get it out of the cupboard his face lights up and he follows you to the room that needs doing. He stands off to one side for much of the time, but comes over regularly (often without being asked) and holds onto the top of the handle while you push it backwards and forwards.

Elaine, team member, Derbyshire

Graded assistance to ensure success

'The goal is success, so it is important to provide the right amount of help. Too much, and the member of staff will take over the activity; too little, and the person will not succeed.'

Mansell *et al*, 2005

Thinking about activities and interactions as a series of steps also helps staff to see how they can vary the type and amount of support they provide at different stages. It is vital that staff know each person well enough to be able to give just the right kind and amount of help at the right time. Too much and the person is 'over-helped' and too little leaves the person faced with a task which is too difficult and complex for them.

Different types and levels of assistance

Different ways of giving support don't all give the same level of help. For example, telling somebody how turn on the washing machine provides a lower level of assistance than guiding his or her hands to the dial and helping them to turn it. We can summarise the types of support into four areas:

- natural cues and consequences
- verbal cues
- visual cues
- physical cues.

The following **table 2** outlines a range of help within each area (from most to least).

Table 2: Different types and levels of assistance		
Natural cues and consequences		
Most	**→**	**Least**
Adding artificial cues and consequences	**Pointing out natural cues and consequences**	**Experiencing natural cues and consequences**
Natural cues and consequences don't have the same potency for some of the people we support. In these situations, we may need to introduce other (artificial) cues and consequences to motivate the person to participate.	Some of the people we support will need to have these natural cues and consequences highlighted.	The majority of activities and interactions in our daily lives have naturally occurring cues and consequences, and experiencing these usually motivate people to participate in them.
Example:		
'Let's clean the dishes, then afterwards we can go and watch your favourite TV programme together.'	Pointing to the dishes on the table and the dishwasher and explaining that the dishes need to be done in order to make the kitchen tidy and have clean plates for tomorrow.	Dirty dishes on the kitchen table after the evening meal are the natural cue and having a clean and tidy kitchen is the natural consequence of cleaning up.

Verbal cues		
Most	**→**	**Least**
Precise step-by-step instruction	**Occasional redirection**	**Hints and tips**
A series of verbal prompts that tell the person what to do a step at a time, guiding them through the sequence of the activity or interaction.	Questions or verbal prompts which redirect the person's actions or movements within the activity or interaction.	Questions or verbal prompts which let the person know that it's time to do something or that something needs to be done.
Example:		
'Pick up the plate', 'Reach down', 'Put it in the rack'.	'Move the plates together a bit more so they all fit in the rack.'	'What shall we do about these dishes?'
Visual cues		
Most	**→**	**Least**
Exact demonstration	**Modelling**	**Point and gesture**
Precise illustration of the specific action or step that needs to be done next.	Providing an example of how the activity could be completed.	Clear gestures or signs which tell the person what to do next.
Example:		
Placing the plate in the rack to show the person how to put their plate next to it.	Loading plates neatly to show how best to load the dishwasher.	Pointing to the plate that needs to go into the dishwasher and then to the place in the rack where it needs to go.

Physical cues		
Most	→	**Least**
Direct physical assistance	**Guidance through objects**	**Touch**
Physical support which assists the person through the entire movement or activity.	Using the object to guide the person through the movement.	Brief physical contact to initiate action, but not support or assist the person through the entire movement.
Example:		
Staff member places their hand on the person's hand, holding the plate and guides them to place it in the dishwasher.	As the person holds the plate the staff member holds the opposite side and moves it towards the dishwasher.	Staff member touches the side of the person's hand, holding the plate and gently nudges towards the dishwasher.

There are a number of levels within direct physical assistance – placing your hand over the person's and guiding their hand gives more help than guidance at the wrist or forearm.

The use of physical cues must be done sensitively and respectfully. It must be done in ways that reflect what that particular person is used to and avoid what they find uncomfortable. Staff can be hesitant about using direct physical assistance, particularly with people with severe learning and physical disabilities and these issues will be explored further in Chapter 12.

Using graded levels of assistance

People like different types of assistance and, wherever possible, staff should use an approach the individual is comfortable with. In particular, some people really don't like hand-over-hand physical guidance and in these circumstances, it may be better to find another way or adapt the activity to reduce the amount of hand-over-hand assistance required.

In practice, the different types and levels can be used together and staff switch back and forth between them depending on the person's needs. The natural cues and consequences are always present and verbal cues are often used in conjunction with visual or physical cues. The aim is to grade the type and level of assistance to provide the person with just enough help. If one level of help is not working then staff need to move on to the next level or add a different kind of help so that the person is successful in the activity.

Staff observation

My manager recently observed me supporting Keith to set the table. When it came to getting the knives and forks out, I brought the cutlery tray over to the table and asked Keith to get a knife out to put next to the place mat. Keith didn't respond in the way he normally does so I asked him again, this time he looked down at the cutlery tray but still didn't pick up the knife. I tried again saying 'Pick up the knife, Keith'. He started to look frustrated but still didn't move to pick up the knife.

I decided I'd better try another way, so I took all the other cutlery out of the tray, pointed to the knives and asked him again. This time he picked up the knife and put it on the table next to the placemat.

During the feedback, the manager asked me what I could have done differently to help Keith be more successful. I said that I could have taken the other cutlery out of the tray earlier. My manager explained how rather than repeating the verbal prompts over and over, I could have pointed to the knives the second time I asked.

In my next supervision meeting, my supervisor explained graded levels of assistance to me and we discussed how I could use these with Keith and the other people we support. I feel much more confident about supporting people now and think I am better prepared to support people when they don't get it right first time.

Sally, team member, York

Maximising choice and control

'... as activities unfold, there are many opportunities to support the person concerned in deciding what to do next.'

Mansell *et al*, 2005

The issues around choice can sometimes lead to confused responses from staff. It is, of course, right that people should be offered as many opportunities to choose, and therefore determine the pattern of their lives, as is possible. But a number of things need to be taken into account when considering people's choices about the kind of activities and relationships they participate in each day.

- Real choice requires experience of a range of alternatives, a person can only choose when there are options available to them. A choice between one activity and another is only real if the person has experience of and can do both.
- People's control of their environment can be severely impaired when they have difficulty understanding or expressing their choices and preferences.
- Living in a home and in the community comes with some responsibilities and as a result the people we support may have a choice about when and how they participate in activities but not whether they will be done at all.
- One of the reasons the people we support consistently choose to do nothing is because they have a history of ineffective support and failure.

When the person being supported refuses to participate in an activity, the interaction staff should use their judgement to decide whether the person is making a real choice not to take part at all, or if they don't really understand what the staff member is offering and are uncertain or fearful about what they are asking them to do.

If an individual we support is consistently choosing to do nothing at all, staff need to take this as a sign that they are not offering sufficiently interesting opportunities, or that the way they are offering or supporting the person is not sufficiently helpful and motivating, rather than a sign that the person is OK.

Things that can help are as follows.

- Broaden people's experience of alternatives by ensuring that they routinely experience a wide range of different activities and interactions.
- Arrange the environment so that the person being supported can control it.
- Take note of and respect individual preferences and choices within activities.
- Give people choices in when, where and how activities and interaction happen.
- Use 'little and often' and 'graded assistance' to ensure people routinely experience success in order to build people's confidence in activities, interactions and the support they receive.

In order for people to be successful they need sufficient support. However, almost any type of support has the effect of reducing the amount of control experienced by the person, e.g. by using a verbal prompt to move onto the next step in an activity we are effectively preventing the person from choosing when to move on by themselves.

A logical extension of this principle is that more support always leads to the person experiencing less control. So it is important to bear this in mind when considering how to maximise the choice and control that people experience. It will always be possible to adapt the use of cues that are effective for the person so as to increase the level of control they experience whilst maintaining the general overall style of support we are using. **Figure 1** demonstrates how these principles can be combined.

Least	Amount of control experienced		Most
Most	**Amount of support received**		**Least**
Natural cues and consequences ➝	Adding artificial cues and consequences	Pointing out natural cues and consequences	Experiencing natural cues and consequences
Verbal cues ➝	Precise step-by-step instructions	Occassional redirection	Hints and tips
Verbal cues ➝	Exact demonstration	Modelling	Point and gesture
Physical cues ➝	Direct physical assitance	Guidance through objects	Touch

Figure 1: Different cues, different levels of support and their combined effect on control

The importance of waiting

Support needs to be provided in a timely fashion which takes account of the person's ability to process what is happening and respond. Difficulties can arise when staff move through activities and levels of support too quickly. The risk of pre-empting people's responses in this way increases when staff have been supporting the person for a long time and are used to interpreting their indirect and unintentional communication.

Effective support requires staff to develop an awareness of their own actions and the points at which they introduce additional prompts and information. They need to know the person well enough to know:

- when are the right times to wait
- how long to wait
- what to wait for.

Staff observation

The team that supports Jessica and Dawn needed a lot of help to work consistently and predictably, so they had a pretty prescriptive shift plan that they worked to. However, after some time, it became clear that they had got stuck and were working inflexibly so that Dawn and Jessica had little control of what happened, and who did what, when. When asked, the staff team would say that they needed to be 'in control' in order to ensure that Jessica and Dawn got what they needed out of life.

To help the staff team explore this, we arranged that on a number of occasions we would deliberately not do anything unless it was led by one of the ladies. We agreed this with Jessica and Dawn, recorded some contingency plans to cover possible eventualities, and it was agreed that I would observe and then discuss the experience with each team member and the ladies.

So over a period of some weeks, each team member had one evening shift where they didn't follow the shift plan but waited [as much as possible] for Dawn and Jessica to take the lead in starting or continuing an activity. Feedback from Jessica and Dawn about these experiences was generally positive – staff were more mixed, some worrying about how much needed to be done, others feeling that this was a more natural way of working. My observations highlighted some individual support issues that needed to be addressed. The most useful lesson for everybody was that by waiting, staff could give considerable power and control to Jessica and Dawn in their day-to-day lives.

Subsequently it was decided to remove the shift plan and ask staff to work more flexibly allowing themselves to be led by the ladies. After this, a new shift plan was introduced – this plan described the range of activities that needed to happen each day, with only some of them being time bound. So now there are plenty of opportunities for Dawn and Jessica to be in control, and staff waiting for them to lead is accepted as good practice.

Niki, team manager, Gloucestershire

Communication

While verbal cues are an important tool in supporting people to participate, excessive prompting or unrelated conversation during activities can be distracting and make it difficult for people to filter information. While social chatting is often intended to put people at their ease, for many people, good support will be reasonably quiet as the staff members let the person do the activity and offers clear and simple prompts to assist them to succeed.

Environments which contain competing sounds, sensations and activities can be a barrier to engagement for many of the people we support. It's often something staff are not aware of as they are used to filtering out things in the environment that are not important (e.g. having the radio on while they make a cake). Recognising this and making appropriate changes can significantly increase the likelihood that the person being supported will successfully participate.

Preparing the materials and environment can also help to communicate to the person what needs to be done and avoids the person having to wait for the activity to start.

Changes in the environment (e.g. the music being turned off and the staff member communicating differently) can also act as a cue to the person that an activity or interaction is about to start.

Key principles to introducing activities

1. **Keep it simple**
   Make sure to get the person's attention first. Then use understandable language and communication aids where appropriate – signs, symbols, photographs or objects of reference. Use body language to give the same message.

2. **Reduce demand and complexity**
   Don't swamp the person with instructions, information or distracting chatter. Make it easy for them to know what is being asked of them and make it easy for them to make a start.

3. **Make the situation speak for itself**
   Have everything ready so that it is clear what is being offered and what the person needs to do.

   Mansell *et al*, 2005

Avoid the teaching trap

There is a danger of staff beginning to treat participation opportunities as teaching programmes. This may be because techniques and tools like task analysis and graded assistance in the past have been associated with teaching programmes and that the planning of support can be very detailed. However, it is important to distinguish between supporting people to participate and teaching it.

It would be undesirable as well as impractical to attempt to teach every single activity in a highly structured way throughout each day. A structured skills-teaching programme only takes a few minutes. Running four different skills teaching programmes will only occupy something like one hour in total per day. Once the person's day has been filled with a variety of activities, it is possible to select two or three key skills to teach at one time.

While it is true that the skills of people we support can increase when they are consistently supported to engage in a range of meaningful activities and relationships, teaching skills are not the primary purpose of person-centred active support. It is important that the need to increase the level of assistance is not seen as failure or as a regression of skills – we all have good days, when we need less support and bad days, where more help is needed to be successful.

Observation

When supporting a team in the north east to implement person-centred active support, we identified a number of naturally occurring situations which we could utilise to increase people's participation.

The team explained that Steve, a young man with severe learning disabilities, who has no verbal communication, frequently sought out cold drinks. The team agreed to respond to this by having a jug of his favourite cordial on the kitchen bench throughout the day. When Steve went to the jug, staff were asked to provide hand-over-hand assistance for him to pour a drink. This worked really well until I received a call one afternoon from a very excited staff member who explained that she had been a bit slow in getting there to help Steve and as a result he had picked up the jug on his own for the first time.

A week later I visited the service and asked how it was going. The team explained that Steve didn't seem to want to drink as much any more. When I asked more, I discovered that the rest of the team had heard about Steve picking up the jug himself and had stopped offering hand-over-hand assistance to do this. They had started to interpret him not picking up the jug himself as a sign that he didn't really want a drink after all.

I explained that Steve may be able to pick up the jug on some days and not on others but this should not stop him getting his drink. We clarified how staff would grade their assistance by waiting to see if Steve would pick up the jug himself and if he didn't they would provide the right hand-over-hand support to help him be successful.

Bev, practice development co-ordinator, United Response

Developing a 24/7 approach

Too often staff see person-centred active support as something that happens at certain times of the day or for specific planned activities. While it may be helpful, even necessary, to start off in this way, real success will only be achieved when staff recognise and utilise the wide range of incidental and planned activities which occur throughout the day (see **figure 2**).

This approach requires staff to see it as their job to be on the constant lookout for things which they can involve people in and to understand that they can try new activities and interactions without having to write it down first.

In order to achieve this, individual staff need to continuously:

■ identify the opportunity for the person(s) they are supporting to participate in an activity or interaction – **spot it**
■ use the opportunity to support the person to participate – **try it**
■ reflect on the experience (by asking themselves what worked and what didn't work and considering what they would do the same or differently next time) – **learn from it**
■ share the experience with colleagues – **share it with everyone else**

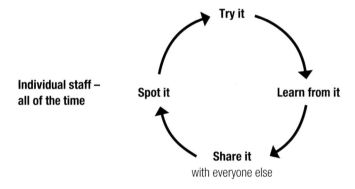

Figure 2: Developing a 24/7 approach – individual staff

This approach also recognises that some activities and support needs should be agreed and recorded in detail by the team in order to achieve consistency, and that this should be specifically reviewed in order to contribute to team learning (see **figure 3**).

Ongoing team work builds on the first cycle by the following.

■ Using the information gathered to identify which activities or types of support need to be agreed in more detail and develop clear and accurate information about how to do this (as discussed in Chapter 5) – **agree it in detail.**

■ Each member of the team presents the activity and provides support in the agreed way to ensure predictability and consistency – **do it consistently.**

■ Identify how well the activity or support is working in practice in order to decide what should stay the same, what should change, and what else we should try – **review it.**

■ Share the learning with colleagues – **share it with everyone else.**

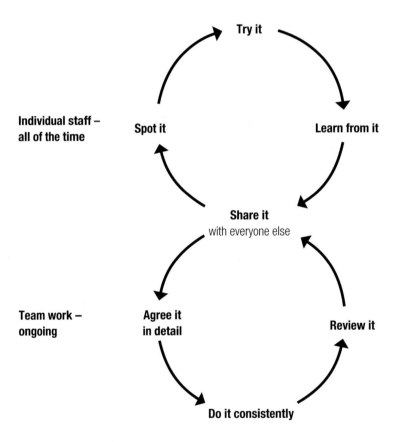

Figure 3: Developing a 24/7 approach – individual staff and team work

Summary

Implementing person-centred active support requires staff to think about activities and interactions differently so that they can see which parts people can do on their own, with staff support and the part staff will do themselves in order to ensure the person experiences success. Each staff member needs to see every moment as having potential and utilise the principles of little and often, graded assistance and maximising choice and control in order to develop an effective environment which maximises the use of naturally occurring engagement opportunities 24 hours a day, seven days a week.

Chapter 4

Increasing predictability

'Everyone needs to know what is likely to happen and when at least to some extent. Predictability is important, both because it helps people work out what they need to do next and because it can reduce their anxiety.'

(Mansell *et al*, 2005)

It is important and reassuring for us to have activities that are predictable and consistent in our lives. Most of us achieve the levels of predictability we require by following routines. Our daily routines, often dictated by work and family commitments, usually involve consistent patterns of activity for getting ourselves to work in the morning and going to bed in the evening; they also become more complex and detailed the more people they involve. Establishing routines in our lives give us greater freedom and flexibility than just taking life as it comes. Routines form a structure for our days, and we fill in the rest of the time around them.

Our routines take account of our unique needs and rhythms, for example 'morning people' generally have routines that are heavier or more intense in the morning and 'night owls' have routines which focus on the evening. We may vary from our routines, either when we want a change or when circumstances dictate, but most of us like some order in our lives.

Observation

I hate ironing, but it all has to be done on the weekend because I work away from home most of the week. I have developed a routine for doing this which works well for me and makes this, my most hated household chore, as painless as possible.

Each Sunday afternoon, after my weekly shopping trip to the supermarket, I set up the ironing in front of the TV in the lounge (ironing board, iron, pile of clothes, hangers etc.) I pour myself a nice glass of wine and put on a 'chick-flick' to enjoy while I'm ironing. I'm always finished by 3pm because that is when I join my friends at our local pub for a drink before Sunday lunch.

Bev, practice development co-ordinator, United Response

While routines and rituals and planning around them are a daily occurrence for most of us, we generally pay them very little attention. This may be why we often fail to recognise the importance of these in the lives of the people we support.

When asked about how much we know about what's happening in our own lives, for example when we'll be having dinner and who will be cooking it, who will be home when we get in from work, when and where we will do our grocery shopping or next see our best friend, we often say we don't know, but after thinking about it a bit more we often do. While it may be hidden, predictability exists in the majority of the things we do and if it's not something we are in control of, we generally have someone in our lives we trust to take care of these things for us.

Observation

I recall talking to a local psychologist about the different approaches taken to daily planning in residential services in our area.

He explained that staff in some services say they don't plan anything because they want to be spontaneous – a kind of 'go with the flow' approach. But what this usually means is that they were disorganised. The people being supported often get ready for activities that then don't happen; or activities stop and start because staff get distracted. Yet other staff seem to plan everything down to the minute detail and then implement the plan in a rigid, mechanical way which means they were not responding to the needs and wishes of the people they are supporting.

> We both agreed that neither of these extremes were sensible or desirable and that what we needed to do was to enable teams to strike the right balance between being adaptable and being organised.
>
> Bev, practice development co-ordinator, United Response

Predictable routines are particularly important for people we support with autistic characteristics or those who have difficulty in understanding other people's intentions, the passage of time and how different parts of their environment operate. If there are large gaps between opportunities to get engaged, or between being asked to take part in an activity and it being ready, the people we support are less likely to be able to maintain their attention and interest.

For people with challenging behaviour, the way the day is organised and the sequence and pace of activity are important. If the person has no way to predict what is going to happen in the next few minutes or hours, if the routines and rituals that are important to them are disturbed or ignored, challenging behaviour is more likely to occur. Recognising the importance of predictability and changing the way we plan and organise routines and activities to be more person-centred can significantly reduce challenging behaviour for some individuals.

Where a group of staff are supporting several people, planning is needed to co-ordinate them to ensure the individuals being supported are not 'lost' when one member of staff thinks someone else is providing support to that individual. Each member of staff needs to know who is supporting which person and how people can move from one thing to another with the support they need.

We have in the past assumed that staff are able to do this kind of co-ordinating and planning as they go along, but now know that this can be complex and require more forward planning. For many teams, it is more practical and realistic to do the bulk of this planning together, in advance, as it reduces the moment-by-moment decisions which need to be made during the shift.

Having a written plan to work from also makes it easier for new and relief staff to work effectively to support people in a range of activities, without having to rely on more familiar staff to direct them throughout the shift.

> ## Observation
>
> I recently visited a service for three people with learning disabilities and severe challenging behaviour in Derbyshire and was delighted to observe well organised person-centred active support. After the observation, I was talking to the team member who was on duty that evening with an agency worker. He had only started working at the service six months before but was very competent and confident about the work he was doing.
>
> He explained that everything he needed to know about how to organise the shift and what activities people were being supported in was on the shift plan.
>
> 'It's all there for you to see and follow. The last place I worked in was absolute chaos, there was no plan for the day and you were just expected to muddle through. It was very stressful and didn't work for the people we were supporting. It was really hard to know what you needed to do and it never felt like you had a successful shift.'
>
> Bev, practice development co-ordinator, United Response

Shift planning

Shift planning refers to a range of tools and formats which are used to schedule the household tasks, personal self-care, hobbies, social arrangements and community activities, individuals' need or want to do each day and to work out the availability of support so that activities can happen predictably.

> ## Shift plans
>
> Let people plan ahead and ensure the right support is available. They help us to work more effectively by:
> - letting people know what is likely to happen and when
> - helping people to prioritise and prepare activities
> - recognising the importance of people's routines and rituals
> - helping to get a balance between predictability and spontaneity
> - giving us and the people we support a plan to be flexible from
> - clarifying the roles and expectations of support staff
> - promoting efficient use of resources
> - providing accountability of action
> - giving us a way of managing when things happen.

Often we don't have to think about our routines and write them down, but there are times, when we don't want to forget things, when we need to plan in changes or when we need to keep others informed and we use diaries or planners to do this. This is more likely to happen when there are a number of people involved (e.g. parents, children, friends and professionals).

For many of the people we support who cannot manage information in this way, when and how things happen is often dependent on other people and factors beyond their control. They often have several different individuals providing support to them who are more influential and bring their own routines and rituals with them.

Staff observation

As part of getting to know the services in my area, I visited the same residential service for three men with learning disabilities on two successive evenings.

On the first night, I arrived as the men came home from the day centre. On arrival, the men were directed to the lounge and the team member brought them each a cup of tea. Once this was finished, each person was supported to have a bath and get changed before dinner, which had been prepared by the team member earlier while the men were at work. These two hours were organised with military precision – people were told what to do and when not involved in these personal care activities were told to sit in the lounge and relax in front of the TV.

The next evening I arrived at the same time to find a different team member on duty. As before, on arrival home from the day service the men were directed to the lounge where they were brought a cup of tea. The team member sat with us, having a drink herself while we watched Neighbours and Home and Away on TV. While she periodically went upstairs to make a few calls about cover for the next few days, she spent the next two hours talking to people about their day and what was happening for the weekend.

At about 6.15pm, I was ready to leave for the evening and I asked her what the plans were for the rest of the evening. I was particularly keen to know what was happening for dinner as I hadn't seen any meal preparation going on. She explained that she didn't feel like cooking tonight and so was going to order a takeaway at 7pm. After dinner she said she would support the men with baths and getting them ready for bed.

I was struck by the different pace and flow of activities in the same house which seemed to be determined only by who was on duty, and I wondered how the three men being supported felt about coming home each day not knowing what to expect or what would be expected of them.

Anonymous, area manager, North East

Many services have individual planners and weekly timetables, like the one in **table 1**, which outlines significant household or community activities. While in some circumstances this level of planning is sufficient, in many services it is insufficiently detailed to result in person-centred routines or high levels of participation in activities on a day-to-day basis.

Table 1: Example of a weekly timetable

	M	T	W	T	F	S	S
Colin	9am – 4pm Oaklands Day Centre	9am – 4pm Oaklands Day Centre	9am – 4pm Oaklands Day Centre		2pm Swimming		10am – 11am Church with mum and sister
Bernard			9am – 4pm Oaklands Day Centre	9am – 4pm Oaklands Day Centre	9am – 4pm Oaklands Day Centre	2pm Lunch at a local pub	
Jane	11am – 2pm Work experience at Morrisons	9am – 3pm Parkside Day Service	12.30 – 3pm Mum's for lunch and shopping		9am – 3pm Parkside Day Service		

Services need to develop effective daily planning systems which co-ordinate the support provided during each shift, assisting staff to ensure there is a balance between planned priorities and changes to routine, which are based on the needs and choices of the people they are supporting.

Observation

During a visit to one of our services in Essex on a hot August afternoon, I arrived to find the staff and one of the four people being supported (Mark), sitting outside in the garden listening to music. The team members explained that they had decided that since it was such a nice day they would leave the normal household chores till later in the evening so they could all enjoy the sunshine.

> They were also planning to have a barbeque for dinner instead of the usual
> shepard's pie that John (one of the four being supported) would normally make
> on his return from the day centre.
>
> Mark was picking grass from the lawn, John was sitting cross legged, rocking
> from side to side on the kitchen floor, Barry was in his bedroom dozing on his
> bed and Paul was carrying a dustpan and brush from room to room.
>
> It soon became clear that the staff had changed the agreed shift plan, which
> was based on the preferred activities and routines of the people being
> supported, because they wanted to enjoy the rare afternoon sunshine. This
> meant that while the team members chatted outside, the people we support
> were confused by the change of routine and were disengaged for long periods
> of time.
>
> Bev, practice development co-ordinator, United Response

These plans should schedule the household tasks, personal self-care, hobbies, social
arrangements and community activities, individuals need or want to do each day and
work out the availability of support so that activities can be accomplished successfully
with maximum participation. We call these shift plans but other terms such as activity
and support plans are also used to describe these planners in other organisations.

Having a shift plan doesn't mean people have to stick to it religiously – it will usually
need to be adjusted throughout the day, for example, to take account of individual
choices, additional changes to planned activities and when things take more or less
time than originally planned. Staff are working to ensure that the flow of activity is
maintained rather than getting hung up on precise timings and task lists.

Developing a shift plan

The following has been adapted from Jones *et al* (1996) *Active Support*. A handbook
for planning daily activities and support arrangements for people with learning
disabilities.

Stage 1 – identifying routines and activity patterns

1. Agree and record, via team meeting and discussion with the people we support,
    all of the personal, household, leisure, social, community and other activities
    which go on in the course of a week. Agree how often, when these things are
    done (see **table 2**).

Table 2: Example of record of weekly activities				
Personal	**Household**	**Work/day activities**	**Leisure/ social**	**Other**
Getting up Brushing teeth Bathing Showering Dressing Blow-drying hair (Jane) Breakfast Coffee Lunch Dinner Evening snack Drink Medication (7am, 12noon, 2pm and 7pm)	Preparing breakfast Clearing away Loading the dishwasher Preparing lunch Setting the table Weekly shopping Daily shopping Laundry Putting wheelie bin out (Tuesday night) Dusting	**Colin** Oaklands – 9–4pm Mon, Tue, Wed **Bernard** Oakland – 9–4pm Wed, Thu, Fri **Jane** Morrison's work experience – 11–2pm Mon Parkside – 9–3pm Tues and Fri	**Colin:** Swimming – 2pm Fri Church with mum and Sue 10–11am Sun **Bernard** Pub lunch – 2pm Sat **Jane** Lunch @ mum's and shopping 12.30–3pm Wed	Health and safety checks Petty cash Handovers

2. Make a note of any significant routines or rituals that are important to the people we support, which need to be incorporated into shift plans e.g. ensuring there is time planned in for Colin to check the doors and windows are locked before leaving the house. Use person-centred thinking tools such as 'good day/bad day' and 'important to/important for' as well as goals from PCP and or reviews to highlight other things that should be incorporated into your planning.

3. Set a timeframe for each day of the week, based on typical times of getting up, going to bed, mealtimes and handovers. These regular activities often act as markers for the people we support and help us to plan other related activities around them, for example, preparing the meal and setting the table before the evening meal with clearing away and loading the dishwasher soon after. These routine activities also divide the day up into time periods into which other activities needed could fit (**table 3**).

Table 3: Example of timeframe for Monday		
Monday		
7am	Colin gets up and has a shower before getting dressed	Bernard gets up, washes his face and brushes his teeth
7.30am	Colin makes his own breakfast of cereal and juice	Bernard is supported to make toast and a coffee
8am	Jane gets up and is supported to have breakfast and then watches TV	
8.25am	Colin is reminded that it is almost time for the minibus to arrive so he can check the windows and doors	Bernard tidies the kitchen and loads the dishwasher
8.30am	The minibus arrives and Colin leaves for Oaklands	Bernard has a shower and gets dressed
9.30am	Jane has a shower and dresses for work	Bernard tidies his room and changes the bedclothes

4. Make a note of any activities that have not been incorporated into this timetable either because they are not frequent or routinely carried out, as these will make up the list of options or additions which can be added to shift plans later (see **table 4**).

Table 4: Example of additional activities	
Options	

Monthly:
  Vehicle check – Colin
	When needed:
	  Mowing the lawn
	  Sweeping the front path
	  Washing windows

5. Check the overall impression of the timetable you have developed so far. Ensure that everything is included; check that the day-to-day balance of activities is OK and that the timings are realistic. Then check the timetables out with the people you support, staff and others to ensure important activities and preferences are not overlooked.

Now you are ready to transfer the information from the weekly timetable onto a daily shift plan covering all or part of the day.

Things to consider when planning the day

- There will be times in the day, or during certain activities where it will be necessary for one member of staff to support more than one person.
- Staff will not necessarily be allocated to work with the same individuals throughout the shift.
- Allocating staff to an area (rather than to individuals) can be a useful strategy to maximise planned and incidental engagement opportunities.

Stage 2 – Designing a shift plan

The shift plan should be designed to ensure staff and the people being supported to know when who is doing what and with whom. It should ensure there is a smooth flow from one task to the other, and that everything gets done, but more critically that the people we support are actively involved.

When designing a shift plan, it is worth checking it against a number of principles to test its effectiveness. This is one way to ensure that it's not just a piece of paper or a document that has just been copied from elsewhere. Using the seven golden rules below also reinforces the idea that there is no bespoke shift plan format, but that its purpose and effectiveness are the key issues.

The seven golden rules of shift planning

A shift plan should:

1. indicate when and who to support doing what
2. include other activities that staff need to do that don't (if only at the moment) involve the people we support
3. allocate support and activities to specific staff
4. indicate how things fit together – across people and across the passage of time
5. be viewed flexibly and include options or contingency plans
6. be only as detailed as they need to be, to ensure organised and smooth running support – in general terms less detail is needed when less staff are involved and when people being supported are more able to organise their own lives.

A shift plan must:

7. be reviewed in light of what we find – what works and what doesn't.

The look and level of detail in shift plans will vary, with the most successful systems being developed within the service to meet the specific needs of the people being supported and the staff team.

Example 1: from the Welsh Centre for Learning Disabilities

Here, the basic routines, regular activities and tasks are agreed in advance and recorded on a daily shift-planning sheet. Team members then review these plans daily adding additional tasks and activities where possible, planning how to deploy themselves to support people effectively.

Figure 1: Example of a shift plan from the Welsh Centre for Learning Disabilities

Time	Olive	SW	Roger	SW	Ann	SW	Household	Options
7.00am	Get up, wash, dress	AJ	Get up, wash, dress Prepare breakfast	CE	Get up, wash, dress (on own) Set table		Put bins out Set table	
8.00am	Breakfast	AJ	Breakfast	CE	Breakfast	CE	Clear breakfast	Good walk
8.30am	Clear breakfast		Wash-up/load dishwasher		Start laundry		Wash-up/load dishwasher	Water plants
9.00am	Shopping	CE	Clean bedroom and bathroom	AJ	Shopping/post office collect benefit and pay bills	CE	Start laundry	Gardening
10.00am			Laundry	AJ	Finish laundry			Cut the grass
	Unpack groceries	CE	Coffee and visit from mother	Mrs F		AJ	Unload dishwasher and stack coffee cups	Polish furniture
11.00am	Coffee				Coffee			Clean windows
	Gardening	CE	Physiotherapy	FG				
12.00pm	Cut the grass	CE	Unload dishwasher and stack coffee cups	AJ	Prepare lunch	AJ		

Example 2: from United Response

Here the team has agreed a more detailed plan of activities and team member roles have been allocated in advance (at the top of the plan). Throughout the shift, team members check their responsibilities and agree any changes (including things added from the options list) with each other and the people they are supporting.

Figure 2: Example of shift plan from United Response

Time	Team member A	Team member B	Team member C	Options
7.00am	Handover Support Duncan to come downstairs	Support anyone who is up to have breakfast		Put recycling bins out
7.15am	Support people to get up and have breakfast			Gardening
10.00am		Support Carol to have bath spa	Support Duncan to put the recycling bins out	
10.30am		Support Mandy to hoover and check the laundry		
11.00am	Support Andrea to go out for a county walk and pub lunch	Support Garry to fill up nut container for the birds Drop off wrongly delivered mail to no. 27	Support Duncan to go for a walk in the village	Drop off wrongly delivered mail to no. 27 Help Mandy to complete her college application form
11.30am		Support everyone to have a drink	Support Caroline to make a drink for everyone	
11.45am		Help Mandy to complete her college application form	Support Caroline to make lunch	
12.15pm		Support Mandy to lay the table		

Whatever format you decide to use, it needs to be simple to follow and should avoid using jargon and abbreviations which may not be understood by all. Having a set format on the computer can make it easier to amend and reproduce shift plans when changes are made.

For many people we support, shift plans or the part of the plan which impact on them can be organised and presented in ways they can access and find useful to work out what will happen next, see **figure 3**.

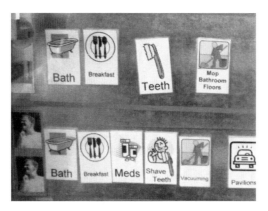

Figure 3: Example of pictorial shift plan

Once you have completed the shift plan, you should use the 'unfamiliar competent worker test' to double check the content and format, i.e. could a reasonably competent support worker who has never worked here before use this shift plan to support people effectively for this shift?

Implementing the shift plan

Once the shift plan has been developed, staff need to use the plan everyday. While handovers may seem the most logical place for planning the shift ahead, they are not the most naturalistic and can limit the involvement of the people being supported.

While staff may take some time at the beginning of the shift to talk to each other and map out how they are going to support people, there are also some natural planning points during the day which can be utilised to involve everyone. For example, using the time when people return home from work or day activities and are relaxing or chatting over a cup of tea to plan what's happening before supper, at supper and planning out the next morning.

These short discussions are used to review what has been already planned or needs to change and to determine who will be doing what with whom. The plan (written or pictorial) can then be altered to reflect what's been agreed.

As with any change in working practices, the introduction of a shift plan will need to be led and its implementation monitored. This will require shift leaders and managers to ensure:

■ everyone has accurate information about the plan

■ all staff understand their responsibility to implement the plan consistently

■ that any additional resources and or support needed to implement the plan and train staff is provided

■ staff receive regular modelling, coaching and feedback on their performance and information about the effectiveness of the shift plan

■ outcomes and feedback from staff and the people we support are used to modify the shift plan quickly so it remains 'live'.

Reviewing the shift plan

Keeping the plan 'live' is key to its use and success. The team will need to track changes in the person's involvement and confidence within activities and look for ways to continue to improve the plan and support they provide.

Planning in this way can seem complex and you won't always get it right first time. The very best shift plans will need to be tweaked – timings won't always be quite right, people may feel too rushed or be waiting for long periods on particular days. People and activities should also change over time – seasons change, community activities stop and start for a variety of reasons, people develop new interests or want to try different things.

It is therefore important to monitor the use and outcomes of the shift plan and the activities within it in order to identify what is working and not working for the people we support and the staff team, and make the changes needed to ensure it remains person centred.

Summary

Effective implementation of person-centred active support requires services to develop a daily planning system which provides a way to schedule the household tasks, personal self-care, hobbies, social arrangements and community activities that individuals need or want to do each day. It also aims to work out the availability of support so that activities can be accomplished successfully with maximum participation. Routines that are based on an individual's preferences, needs and the way they want to live their lives must be at the heart of strategies that are designed to promote predictability.

Predictability requires events and activities. Once we recognise how important it is to deliver predictability, we have to provide person-centred events and activities that happen across time, which the people we support can experience and understand, even if that feels like lots of things are happening. Not only does this enable increased levels of engagement, as discussed in Chapter 1, it also gives the people we support the consistent patterns of activity, routines and structure which we all have and need to gain greater freedom and flexibility in our lives.

Chapter 5

Increasing consistency

'Consistency – being treated the same way by the different people providing support – is important for most people. It matters because everyone providing support ought to be doing so in the way the person they are helping prefers or is most comfortable with. If different people do things in different ways, it can also make it harder for the individual to work out what he or she needs to do.'

(Mansell *et al*, 2005)

In the previous chapter, we looked at predictability – how to enable everyone to know what is likely to happen and when, as well as how we can make the flow of activities seamless. In this chapter, we will look at consistency – how to ensure people are supported in the same way by different staff.

Consistency – being treated in the same way by the different people providing support is important for most people. It matters because everyone providing support ought to be doing so in the way the person they are helping prefers or is most comfortable with. If different people do things in very different ways, it can also make it harder for the individual to work out what he or she needs to do.

Observation

Recently our credit card company contacted us to query a couple of suspicious transactions. They asked if we had bought lighting equipment in Dubai and then tried to purchase something else in Mexico a day later. I said that as it happens our life is not that exciting, and so the transactions were listed as fraudulent.

The lady on the phone informed us that as one of the transactions had gone through we would need to report it once it appeared on a statement, so that we could be reimbursed. The money would not be returned unless I did this. I objected – surely they already knew that this was fraudulent activity, otherwise we wouldn't be having the conversation in the first place, but I was told that it had to come from me otherwise the money couldn't be reimbursed.

Over the next five days I rang the credit company daily. What followed was a familiar catalogue of being given the wrong number, getting lost between departments, being told one thing one day and the opposite the next. Also, one day I was heavily questioned about my identity, and later in the same week they went straight into conversation without checking who I was.

My experience was of being disorientated and disempowered. I had no secure grounding on which to base my understanding of what was going on. And crucially by the fourth day, I still hadn't been able to actually report the fraudulent transaction.

On day five, I made my final attempt only to be told that the money had already been reimbursed earlier in the week. You can imagine my reaction.

What made me rage and despair was not that they had rules but that they kept changing. I was being to told something different each time. Each operator insisted on different procedures and consistency was certainly needed.

John, practice development advisor, United Response

There are two areas to consider when looking at consistency for the people we support, as highlighted in **table 1**.

Table 1: Consistency of support and activities

Consistency of support	**Consistency within activities**
Different staff can provide different help in different ways – leaving the person being supported confused and getting inconsistent support.	Different staff can do different activities in different ways – leaving the person being supported confused about what they are doing and less confident about how to do it next time.

This can mean the person being supported by a staff team of six needs to learn six different ways of doing one activity, and has to be able to adapt or tolerate six different ways of being supported. The person being supported has to work quite hard and there is an increased chance that they will fail.

Observation

When I was due to visit Chloe, a person we support in Manchester, I was warned that my arrival would coincide with the return of a team member (Frances) from a month off, and that Chloe generally reacted badly to a member of staff in these circumstances. I was also told by another staff member that all of the team were strong individuals and all worked differently with Chloe.

As it happened, I observed Chloe and Frances make a cup of tea between them. This took a long time (about 20 minutes) with Frances having to provide lots of prompts, encouragement and waiting before Chloe would respond. A bit later, Chloe needed to get changed and I could hear that the process of removing clothes, choosing and putting on clean ones also took a similar period of time, with again lots of prompts, encouragement and waiting.

Some time later, Chloe and Frances made another cup of tea and subsequently Chloe needed to get changed again. Both activities took about five minutes with Frances needing to provide much less direct support and Chloe responding with certainty and confidence to the prompts and encouragement she was given.

It was clear that the activities were not new to Chloe, nor did she specifically lack skills in these areas. What seemed to be going on was that Chloe was struggling to come to terms with the variety of ways that staff were supporting her. That was why she had so much difficulty with staff who she hadn't seen for a while, and why things improved over a shift as she became accustomed to the support style of each team member.

John, practice development advisor, United Response

We therefore need to establish with the people being supported their preferred way of doing things and we need to make it incumbent on staff to adopt this pattern rather than expect the person to change according to who is on duty each day.

Consistency of support within activities is particularly important for some people with learning disabilities, especially those with autistic characteristics or those with difficulty in understanding. The level of consistency required will vary from person to person: we need to find the 'Goldilocks' level of consistency for each individual we support – not too much, not too little, but just enough. Sometimes it's important to distinguish between consistency of support and consistency of activity, and consistency of support is often more important than consistency of activity. With good support, people can often cope with minor changes to the order of activities and the materials used.

When faced with the issue of consistency, many services end up producing a multitude of written plans (such as an activity or teaching plan). This approach is neither practical nor effective in developing participation opportunities as it requires the implementation of hundreds of instructional documents into staff's everyday interactions with the people they are supporting.

While this approach may be necessary initially, when staff teams need more help on how to involve people in activities, the aim is to get staff to the point that they can use the principles of active support and what they know about the support plan or profile of an individual, to work out how to involve them in whatever activity is going on.

When we take into account the amount of time it takes to produce and update a large number of individualised documents and the amount of time staff spend re-reading the plans to refresh their memory, we see that this approach will significantly reduce the time staff have available to provide hands-on support.

Observation

At a support service for two people in the north east of England, a member of staff was asked how activities were planned, and I was led into the dining room where a folder three inches thick for each person was handed to me. Inside I found a full-task analysis and support guide for each activity detailed in the shift plan (approx 40 plans per person). Each plan had a monitoring form incorporated into the document where staff were required to tick the level of prompt used on each step in the activity.

When I asked how this system worked in reality, the staff reported that there was no way they could remember all the plans and there wasn't time to look at each plan before or during the activities. They explained that they usually went through the folder at the end of each shift and ticked the forms with no real accuracy just to keep the manager happy.

Bev, practice development co-ordinator, United Response

As well as overwhelming staff with paperwork, this approach often disrupts the flow of activities for the people we support and limits the use of new and incidental opportunities for participation outlined in Chapter 3.

Maximising opportunities for the people we support to participate in activities with the right level of consistency often requires a more practical approach to organising support which ensures the following.

- The number of activity and or teaching plans in use at any one time is realistic and does not overwhelm staff with instructions and forms to complete.
- Staff have good information about how people like to be supported in a wide range of activities.
- Staff know how to organise and present activities to maximise people's involvement, control and understanding of the activity.

A more practical approach will include the development of service standards, support profiles and a small number of specific teaching or support plans.

Developing service standards

People often have different standards and different ways of going about their household tasks. The staff team may have, individually or collectively, developed particular standards or rules about how things should be done and look, which are in conflict with the needs and preferences of the people they are supporting. This may not be intentional and is unlikely to be written anywhere but will be unwritten, informal rules, or part of the culture of the service. Sometimes people feel quite strongly that their way is the correct way and over time get colleagues and the people they support to conform to their way of doing things. Getting things done as quickly and efficiently as possible to ensure everything is done before the end of the shift is a common unwritten rule in many services.

Observation

On an afternoon visit to a residential service in the south west, I saw one staff member checking on and complaining about the way things had been done on the morning shift. The laundry hadn't been sorted correctly and they hadn't used fabric conditioner, the shirts hadn't been folded in the right way, the bathroom hadn't been cleaned properly.

I found myself thinking 'there'll be hell to pay'. Sure enough, she wrote a number of comments about the things she'd found in the communication book and told me she'd be having a word with the individual staff members the next time she was on shift with them.

Bev, practice development co-ordinator, United Response

In order to develop consistent opportunities, and therefore opportunities for the person being supported to become less dependent on staff, it is useful for the team to develop standard approaches to routine household activities.

As described in Chapter 4, predictability of when and where regular household activities take place can be achieved through the development of shift planning. Developing service standards requires the team to agree how these activities will be carried out and to what standard.

This approach often means some staff have to re-learn well-practised skills but it is easier for staff to learn one new method than for the people they are supporting to learn several methods.

For our approach to be person centred, decisions about how things will be done must be informed by, and matched as closely as possible to, the routines, standards and choices of the people being supported.

Observation

During a visit to the home of three young men we support in Brighton, I noticed that there were empty cups, beer cans and full ashtrays in the lounge, the carpet and kitchen floor were looking decidedly grubby and there was a stack of dishes in the sink. The support worker explained that the men, in their late teens and early 20s, were adamant that housework wasn't a priority.

'They do a clean up every couple of weeks (vacuuming, mopping the floors and a bit of dusting) but otherwise they are happy to do things as and when they need to. This can mean that the dishes don't actually get done until there are no clean ones left. It's taken quite a while for some people on the staff team to accept this but it is their house. I know guys in their 20s without disabilities whose houses always look a mess.'

Bev, practice development co-ordinator, United Response

The team should also identify and wherever possible select the options which provide the most opportunities for people to participate.

Staff observation

When agreeing our standards for evening meals, we looked at setting the table and came up with the following possibilities.

1. Table set with tablecloth, napkins, place mats, plates, glasses, knives, forks and spoons. Cold drinks served in jugs and food served in individual serving dishes.

Person-centred active support: A handbook © Pavilion Publishing (Brighton) Ltd 2010

2. Table set with tablecloth, place mats, plates, glasses, knives, forks and spoons. Cold drinks served in jugs and food served in individual serving dishes.
3. Table set with place mats, plates, glasses, knives, forks and spoons. Cold drinks served in jugs and food served in individual serving dishes.
4. Table set with place mats, glasses, knives, forks and spoons. Cold drinks served in jugs and food plated up in the kitchen before being brought to the table.
5. Table set with knives, forks and spoons. Cold drinks served in glasses and food plated up in the kitchen before being brought to the table.

We then asked ourselves, which option best matched the way the people we support like and need things done? And which option provides the best opportunities for the people we support to be involved?

We ended up agreeing to set the table with a tablecloth, place mats, plates, glasses, knives, forks and spoons and to have the cold drinks served in jugs and food served in individual serving dishes so that people could serve themselves at the table.

I've noticed that more often than not, our service standards are the options that include more steps and take longer because these tend to offer the most opportunities for people to get involved. Sure there are quicker and easier ways to do things but it's not about saving time – it's about taking the time to do things with people.

Jane, service manager, Yorkshire

Developing service standards in this way means that everything doesn't need to be written into a formal procedure or plan. The team agree the standards together and support each other to implement them, and new staff learn in the same way they learn many other routines and standards in the work place.

Developing support profiles

Support profiles are a way to capture the long-standing knowledge that staff have, often only in their heads, as well as a team's growing knowledge and skills in supporting people effectively. It is a statement for each individual of what works best for them. It is rather like an activity plan but instead of being for a specific activity or task, it is a general set of principles that will be useful in most situations.

Developing support profiles enables staff to utilise all activities, planned and unplanned throughout the day as participation opportunities, and avoids valuable staff hours being spent developing documentation for support and training plans.

Most of us have preferred ways of receiving information and direction, and being recognised or rewarded for things we have done. Support profiles provide detailed information about the support preferences and interaction styles of the people we support. The information is generalised so that it can be used when supporting the individual in any activity or task.

Staff observation

When looking at ways to develop better support for people, we initially focused on developing support plans for the in-house and the community activities the people we support are routinely involved in. We put together three different formats for these plans and got to work. After a few weeks, myself and the two senior support workers had produced over 80 support plans for the five people we support.

At about this time, I took some of the completed plans along to share at a practice development meeting in the area, where we got into a discussion about how practical this approach was in practice and the amount of work it had taken to produce these plans. One of the other managers at the meeting showed me the 'how I like and need my support' profiles she had been developing. This seemed like a much more realistic and less time-consuming approach.

Since then, the team has worked together to collate what we already know about how people like to be supported, what works best and as a result have developed a support profile for each person we support. Once these were in use, we reviewed the support plans and found that only 10 are still needed. It saves hours of typing up plans and has helped staff to be more confident supporting people in a range of activities and situations.

Gary, service manager, Harrogate

Developing support profiles involves constructing a clear profile, utilising and collating information from existing support plans and other person-centred documents such as communication profiles and plans, likes and dislikes, good day/bad day, important to/ important for things to consider when developing a support profile (see **table 2**).

Table 2: Things to consider when developing a support profile		
Background	■ Are there cultural or historical factors that affect the person's ability or willingness to get involved, for example, experiences of choice, involvement, expectations? ■ Will the person benefit from routine scheduling of activities? ■ What should you avoid or be sensitive to?	
Activities	■ What are the person's preferred activities? ■ What types of activities does the person like or understand best? ■ Are there any particular activities to avoid? ■ Are there particular times of day to avoid? ■ Are there events or interests that the activities should be linked to? ■ Does activity need to be presented in the middle of another positive event?	
Preparation	The activity ■ Is any special preparation required? ■ Do activities need to be set out in any particular way or sequence? ■ Are any aids or adaptations required? ■ Do you need to change the environment or manage noise?	The person ■ How should you invite the person to engage in an activity? ■ How do you explain the size of the task?
Communication	■ How much does the person understand speech, symbols, situation and what is their preferred method? ■ How do you tell them what is coming next? ■ How do you give instructions or information? ■ How do you tell the person that the task is beginning and ending? ■ How do you get information from the person? ■ What do they like interacting or talking about? ■ Do you need to achieve eye contact? If so, how do you get this? ■ Do you need to keep verbal communication to a minimum? ■ What tone of voice and body language do you need to use?	

Table 2: Things to consider when developing a support profile (continued)	
Support during activities	■ Does the person prefer small, frequent opportunities or a longer period of engagement? ■ What kind of support does the person generally need? ■ What kind of support do they prefer and what don't they like? ■ Generally, how can you increase the level of support to ensure success in a way that this person finds helpful? ■ If this person needs reassurance or a boost to their confidence, how should you provide this? ■ Are there any special aspects of supporting this person, for example, where you stand, how you talk to them?
Maximising choice and control	■ How can you support the person to have as much control as possible over the course of activities?
Responding to challenging behaviour	■ Are there situations or triggers to avoid? ■ What is the best way to respond if the person shows challenging behaviour?
Motivation	■ What does the person find motivating or reinforcing about engagement in meaningful activity and relationships? ■ Do you need to offer reassurance, praise and encouragement as well, and if so, how?

Support profiles should be easy for staff to access and follow. Producing and presenting this information using pictures and symbols can make them more accessible to the person being supported and to staff. Some services have found that using video, photos and multi-media formats have enabled the person being supported to be actively involved in training staff how to support them effectively.

Once developed, it is important that the use of the profiles is agreed and monitored. All team members should be coached in their use in a range of situations and be encouraged to continue to build on the information they contain. As with any person-centred information, support profiles need to be regularly reviewed and modified to reflect new learning about what is working and not working for the individual and changes to a person's skills and preferences.

Developing a small number of specific activity or teaching plans

Plans which set out the ways staff will present an activity or teach a skill are valuable when activities need to be more structured or when activities need to be specifically set up or done with particular consistency (see **table 3**).

Person-centred active support: A handbook   © Pavilion Publishing (Brighton) Ltd 2010

Table 3: Activity and teaching plans	
Activity plans	**Teaching plans**
Set out how to go about supporting an individual in a particular activity.	Set out the ways to teach a person to do a skill over a period of time.
By providing information on: ■ the activity and the steps within it ■ the type or level of support needed at each step. Instructions for: ■ presenting the activity ■ supporting the person ■ maximising the person's control ■ reinforcement ■ managing risk.	By providing information on: ■ long-term goal ■ teaching target ■ frequency of teaching ■ rate of success required to move onto the next step. Instructions for: ■ materials and preparation ■ introduction and support ■ reinforcement. A record of: ■ when and who carried out the teaching session ■ the person's correct and incorrect responses during the teaching session.

Teaching plans are a way to help people become gradually more independent over time. The skill being taught is broken down into a series of steps and the way to teach each step is carefully worked out.

Activity plans are useful when there are particular risks involved in an activity or on the occasions where we know we've all got to be very consistent. Activity plans can be used as the basis for risk assessment and risk management to ensure you are managing the risks appropriately while supporting the person to engage in meaningful activities and relationships.

Both of these approaches to planning activities involve some form of task analysis. It can be useful to get staff to practice this way of looking at activities so that it can be generalised to become part of their day-to-day practice.

Task analysis – a useful thing to learn

Task analysis is the skill of being able to see each task as a series of steps or subtasks. It enables staff to identify the parts of activities the person they are supporting could be involved in, and to vary the type and amount of help they offer at different stages.

Breaking tasks down in this way doesn't need to be complicated or recorded in detail in files and reports, but it can need practice. Staff should be encouraged to look at the things that are going on or need doing around them throughout the day, think through the steps involved and how they can support the people around them to participate.

Once they have identified the steps or opportunities within the activity, then they can identify:

■ which steps the person being supported can carry out successfully alone
■ which steps the person could do with help
■ which steps are too difficult for the person to complete and will therefore be carried out by the staff member.

Activity plans can also be used to help staff understand the support preferences and needs of the individuals they are supporting. These details are needed for the development of support profiles.

Using video to record and share how people like to be supported in particular activities can also be a useful way to avoid complex and lengthy paper plans. They are particularly effective because written instructions are often not as easy to follow as watching someone providing good support.

Because of the need to keep the number of written plans to a minimum, reviewing and replacing activity and teaching plans is particularly important. Teaching plans should be revised regularly and removed when the person being supported has learned the required skills and is routinely carrying out the activity as independently as possible. Similarly, activity plans should be removed once the activity becomes routine and risks have been reduced to minimal.

Pulling it all together

The use of service standards, support profiles and a small number of activity or teaching plans alongside other person-centred information, such as person-centred plans, positive behaviour support plans and communication profiles can promote consistent person-centred support.

Staff observation

As part of my work helping staff and managers in United Response's Leeds and Harrogate services to develop easy to access information on how to support people well, we have used information in existing files to create an 'information power pack' for each person we support. Each 'power pack' contains the individual's:

- one page profile
- communication profile
- support profile
- weekly schedule
- important information or procedural details for some specific activities
- details of any important personal care routines
- eating and drinking profile (if required)
- positive behaviour support guidelines.

These 'power packs' enable staff to access the most up-to-date information on how to support people effectively. More comprehensive and detailed records continue to be held in the person's individual file, which staff can also access if needed.

Staff report that this system makes it easy to access and review information on how to support people and say that it is particularly useful for new and relief staff or when regular staff are returning from leave.

Sue Stokes, relief manager, Harrogate

Whatever tools or systems you use to develop consistency, remember that the written plans aren't the most important thing. The important thing is thinking through the issues, and the important result is that the person is supported to engage in meaningful activities and relationships.

Summary

Consistency is an important element of person-centred active support, requiring staff to both establish with individuals their preferred ways of doing things, and to adopt them. The tools and systems that teams use to develop consistency have, in themselves, no great significance. Teams learn a lot from thinking through the issues, but what really matters is only ever that the person is supported to engage in meaningful activities and relationships.

Chapter 6

Promoting team work

'Team meetings are the place to review how well the team is doing in enabling the people the team serves to engage in meaningful activity and relationships. They provide an opportunity to review the balance of activities, the consistency of approach and the pursuit of the goals of inclusion, independence and choice.'

Mansell *et al*, 2005

Having a time when team members can meet together is essential to the implementation of person-centred active support. This time should be utilised to review the activities and relationships those being supported experience and to identify ways to continue to improve the support being provided. Staff need to be clear about what is expected of them, they need to understand what to do and ask for clarification when they don't. Person-centred active support recognises that those being supported need consistency and predictability. This means it is important that staff have a forum to agree approaches and practices. Such team meetings should be regular, planned and have minutes written up. However, team meetings are just one way to promote good team working. This chapter explores how team meetings, along with a range of other strategies, can be used to help staff work as an effective team focused on the practice of person-centred support.

Teamwork

'The way a team plays as a whole determines its success. You may have the greatest bunch of individual stars in the world, but if they don't play together, the club won't be worth a dime.'

Babe Ruth, July, 1940

A team is a group of people working together to achieve a common goal – in our case providing high-quality services to a number of individuals with learning disabilities. Teams are more likely to successfully implement person-centred active support when they have a clear and shared sense of purpose – closely aligned to the values of participation and active involvement in a range of activities and relationships – and where the goals of the team have been developed from the person-centred goals and aspirations of the people they are supporting.

The way a team is led has a major impact on the success of the team. An effective team leader creates an environment where people can be successful as a group, fostering positive team dynamics to ensure the team functions effectively and ensuring that the team work together to:

- review the balance of activities, the consistency of approach and the pursuit of the goals of inclusion, independence and choice for each person they support
- celebrate successes and share good practice
- review unsuccessful activities and interactions to identify learning and agree next steps
- identify new activities and relationships the people they support could be involved in
- implement improvements in the support they provide to individuals
- highlight and pass on information about things that need to change that are out of their control
- develop service systems and tools to be more effective and person centred.

Practice leaders need to be proactive in developing an effective team environment. There are several ways practice leaders can help service teams become more effective.

1. **Establish objectives together:** define performance objectives with the team and make sure that all team members understand the objectives and what action needs to be taken to achieve them.
2. **Develop a participatory style:** encourage staff to suggest ways to improve support. Listen to their ideas and acknowledge their points of view. Encourage team members to discuss issues and to find solutions together.
3. **Focus on contributions:** define objectives for having all team members actively contributing to meetings and discussions. Introduce team members to ways in which they can participate.
4. **Organise meetings:** hold meetings with the whole team which are interesting and focused, where individuals are encouraged to discuss current issues and concerns and identify solutions.
5. **Organise the team:** define roles and responsibilities together. If everyone has a clear role, individuals will be less likely to become frustrated and will be more willing to work together.

6. **Explain the rules:** discuss all expectations and standards that have been established within the service. Explain the rationale for these and discuss their implications in day-to-day practice.

7. **Promote team responsibility:** encourage members of the team to take responsibility for completing specific tasks and to solve problems as a team.

8. **Establish time commitments:** schedule when and how each team member will devote time to team work. Determine if team work will require staff to take on extra work, for example, key workers collating, summarising and analysing information, as discussed in Chapter 10, and, if so, discuss this with all staff to obtain their commitment.

Clarifying expectations

Unclear expectations are common in service teams and can result in interpersonal conflict between team members; resentment and blame; and important activities being missed or duplication of effort around an activity.

Services for people with learning disabilities have changed massively in the past 40 years. One of the hallmarks of this change has been the adoption of an enlightened set of values underpinning the work of staff teams. Operational policies are now informed by a values base which promotes opportunities, support, community involvement, participation and empowerment as the purpose of services.

The work we do is guided by sets of principles or goals that are spelled out in a range of documents from the *Five Service Accomplishments* (O'Brien & Tyne, 1981) to those set out in government policy documents such as Valuing People (Department of Health, 2001), *The same as you?* (Scotland Department of Health, 2000) and *Fulfilling the Promises* (Wales National Assembly Learning Disability Advisory Group, 2001).

Beliefs about fairness and rights have radically altered the way society views and treats people who have previously been excluded and such philosophical ideas are important. However, as philosophy is about ideas and words, there can be a number of problems when using them at service level.

■ It's harder for people to understand each other and to know whether they truly agree.
■ It can be difficult to understand how they translate for people with complex needs and profound disabilities.
■ It's harder to know how to use them everyday.
■ They may seem irrelevant when a crisis comes.

And sharing a belief is not necessarily the same thing as sharing a knowledge of what to do.

Tensions in teams arise when individuals within it presume that 'Everyone else expects what I expect, in the way I expect it'. We all know that people are different but frequently we do not actually translate the theory into clear expectations to explore whether others do in fact subscribe to it. When people's expectations are consistently not met, they feel irritated. Unclear and non-specific expectations are sometimes the basis of conflict within teams. Developing clear expectations within teams creates a climate of open communication and enables constructive assertive behaviour between team members.

Using service statements

A service statement specifies, what we do, how we do it, why we do it and is a useful way to clarify values and direction. It describes the key methods of the service – how it goes about doing what it does. Service statements are helpful because different people have different ideas about what they should be doing at work and because of the influence of ideology it's not always easy for support workers to know in actual terms:

■ what their manager expects of them
■ what their colleagues expect of them
■ what the service as a whole expects of them.

And it's easy for people to use similar words for what they believe in, while doing quite different things.

Developing a service statement requires the team to discuss and record what the organisation's values statements mean in practice for the individuals they are currently supporting and should include information derived from person-centred plans and support profiles (see **figure 1** for extracts from a service statement for a residential service supporting people with profound learning and physical disabilities).

Service statements are documents that act like road maps. They should be a one page document that clearly defines the purpose of the team, how it will work, and what the expected outcomes are.

The service statement should be used:
■ to inform discussions within the service
■ in inductions with new staff
■ when feeding back on performance
■ when discussing the role of the service within the wider organisation
■ to resolve conflicts within the team

- when crises arise
- when decisions are being made around an individual being supported
- when selecting staff
- when planning future developments
- when colleagues need support
- when new referrals are being made
- when clarifying roles and responsibilities within the team.

Service statements need to be reviewed regularly to ensure they remain person centred.

Figure 1: Extracts from a service statement for a residential service supporting people with profound learning and physical disabilities

Our service statement

Staff focus on doing activities 'with' and not 'for' the people they support. We recognise that the people we support have limited experience of activities and successful support and as a result present activities predictably and consistently, not interpreting initial reluctance or resistance as informed choice or individual failure.

Staff understand that for the people they support, resistance can be the first response to new experiences and support, and find ways to work through this to enable people to experience success and move to the next stage of involvement.

People are supported to participate in small parts of activities frequently through the day. Staff make the most of every activity that needs to happen in the home as well as developing a range of community activities and social relationships.

Activities are adapted to ensure movements and materials are close to people and staff use physical assistance (hand-over-hand and guidance through objects) to help people take an active part in the things going on around them. Effective physical support enables participation, sharing and learning and is an integral part of daily routines and practice.

Care is taken when providing personal care to ensure people's individuality and right to privacy is respected at all times. Time is taken to ensure personal care, which is a big part of people's lives, and is a relaxed and inclusive experience.

Routines are based on people's needs and preferences and ensure staff are available when needed and things are not rushed. Consistent routines are used to help the people we support to predict what will be happening around them and reduce fear and anxiety.

Communication methods reflect the fact that people communicate with their emotions to the things they are currently experiencing. Staff attend closely to people's body language, facial expressions and sounds during interactions and activities to enable them to make judgements about how to continue and what to change.

The team recognise that verbal communication is a useful way to create a social and pleasant atmosphere but is not effective for communicating messages or providing support for individuals. When supporting people in activities and relationships, staff use keywords, objects of reference and body language to communicate what is happening now and afterwards.

Intensive interaction is used as a way to develop fundamental communication, as a means of relationship building or as a way of pleasurably spending time with people.

Sensory activities are used to provide simulating experiences and opportunities for people to spend time interacting with the environment and other people within it.

Clarifying roles and responsibilities

Standardised job descriptions can leave staff unclear about their team and individual roles and responsibilities. This can result in:

- differing or unclear expectations
- interpersonal conflicts between team members or the practice leader
- resentment and blame
- important tasks being missed or a duplication of effort around tasks.

When team members are unclear about their roles and responsibilities, teams can find themselves off track or having continuous conflicts. Here are three steps which practice leaders can take to clarify team member's roles.

1. Establish and ensure implementation of standard team roles and responsibilities.
2. Implement strategies for developing and clarifying the team's and each individual's roles and responsibilities.
3. Negotiate deadlines and expectations.

Staff observation

When I first came to the service, I became very frustrated that senior support workers weren't doing enough to lead practice and ensure staff developed consistent ways of working. But during my first senior's meeting, I discovered that no one had explained what was required.

We spent some time in meetings discussing what they needed to do and I followed this up in supervision (using information from the meetings and using the competencies framework). We focused on the actions and behaviours they needed to use when supervising and coaching other team members, what they were expected to do to lead the shift and their responsibilities for reviewing the involvement of the people we support.

Spending the time clarifying their roles and responsibilities has really paid off. It's enabled me to identify people's individual strengths and address some people's training and development needs, so I can help them to develop the skills and confidence they need to do their jobs better.

Julie, service manager, York

Learning from each other

Effective teams share information, insight, experience, and tools about the people they are supporting and the activities and relationship they are supporting people to participate in. Team members help each other solve problems, give each other advice, and develop new approaches or tools for more and more effective support. Regularly helping each other makes it easier for teams to show their weak spots and learn together in meetings. As they share ideas and experiences, people develop a shared way of doing things, a set of common practices. Sometimes they formalise these in guidelines and standards, but often they simply remain 'what everybody knows' about good practice.

When team members work together and share common goals, team members easily share the information and thinking. By focusing on supporting people in a range of activities and relationships, teams can develop a real sense of common purpose and focus. By working together in close proximity over an extended period, they develop a rhythm, rapport and common identity, improving their ability to build on each other's ideas and solve problems.

To learn, staff need both time to reflect and a safe environment in which to do it in. They need time to think about their experience and its implications, and incorporate new insights into their current ways of working with the people they support. They need safety to explore new ideas and challenge their own assumptions. When they develop trust and rapport, staff can feel safe enough to share their thinking, the reasons behind their conclusions, the questions they have about their conclusions and even their undeveloped ideas. When they take time to collectively reflect on their experience, they can build on each other's ideas and deepen the richness of their thinking and insights.

Team meetings

Team meetings provide a forum to:

- promote the importance of engagement and person-centred approaches
- give clear information about practice
- share information and solve problems
- acknowledge and celebrate successes and good practice
- give feedback on performance
- review the extent of engagement in meaningful activities and relationships by the people they support
- review current practice and support arrangements
- develop consistent approaches to support
- identify opportunities to develop existing and introduce new activities and relationships.

Supporting people to actively participate in a wide range of activities and relationships is complex, so it is important that team members have a forum in which they can raise concerns for discussion if they think things are not working as well as they should.

Team meetings provide regular opportunities to review progress for each of the people being supported, noting success, resolving problems and working out new arrangements. While it is not realistic to expect that staff and organisational issues will not be part of team meetings, care needs to be taken to prevent them from dominating. Dealing with issues about the people we support first, before dealing with organisational communication and staff issues, makes it more likely that proper attention is given to needs and preferences of those being served.

Role play

Using role play to encourage learning about successful support skills can be very powerful. It allows all kinds of difficult situations to be covered in a relaxed environment, enabling staff to become moderately skilled before they need to provide support to people who may find clumsy support harder to tolerate. Role play encourages staff to discuss the difficulties raised, to consider how best to handle them and to retain this learning.

Confident and competent support workers can work together performing a role play of a new or different aspect of an activity and support plan with other team members observing and asking questions. Alternatively, it can be useful to get people working in groups to produce a short role play demonstrating one aspect of support. The group can decide on whether they will show the team member struggling or failing to provide appropriate support, or to show them supporting the person to participate in the activity well.

Role play can also provide an opportunity for team members to practice particular support techniques, for example positioning, communication, etc. Working in pairs or in threes, with one person observing and providing feedback, team members take on the role of support worker and individual being supported and practice using the appropriate support for particular activities or interactions. This approach enables team members to try out the support they are expected to provide and receive immediate feedback and support.

When using role play in meetings, it is important to allow people a short time to prepare and to take time to draw out what those watching have observed and what they have learned after each role play.

Staff observation

At a recent team meeting, we discussed the new activities we wanted to introduce for the people we support following person-centred reviews. The team was keen to do this but a number of staff were worried about the physical assistance they would need to use in order to support Mark to participate in peeling the potatoes. They were scared of getting it wrong and using too much pressure.

We split up into pairs and used role play to test out various ways to lay the activity out, position ourselves and Mark, and provide the hand-over-hand assistance. We all fed back what we found worked and didn't work, and agreed how we would all do it from now on. We finished the session by role playing this final version.

The staff were not keen when I first suggested the role play but it helped us to identify the best approach and gave everyone a chance to practice and experience the activity from both perspectives first hand.

Julie, service manager, York

Use of video

The development of person-centred active support emphasises the importance of consistent ways of supporting people to participate in a wide range of meaningful activities and relationships, rather than expecting the person being supported to adapt to a number of different approaches, depending on who is on duty. Video is an obvious and useful means of communicating the required approach to a number of staff at the same time.

Video can provide an extremely useful means of assisting and promoting communication, engagement and inclusion by and with the people we support.

When training staff in the skills and methods specific to a service and individual, video can be an extremely helpful tool to complement, assist and improve the support provided. There may also be times when videos can prove helpful in meetings or discussions about the individual, for example:

- in annual or person-centred reviews
- as information for parents or carers
- as information for other professionals.

When planning the use of video, it is essential to consider the potential for intrusion, issues relating to consent, and the intended benefits. Before filming can take place, organisational standards and procedures regarding the use of video must be in place and will include the following principles.

- The consent of people being recorded should be obtained, and the purpose of the film and subsequent use explained. Where a person lacks the capacity to give their consent, any recording must be demonstrated to be in their best interest.
- Nothing should be filmed that could be regarded as intrusive or demeaning.
- Video must not be used for anything that could be construed as voyeurism.
- Confidentiality must be respected and individual dignity preserved.
- Records regarding the content, purpose, benefits, consent, responsibilities, storage and disposal must be kept appropriately.

Risk assessment

A risk assessment should be carried out and recorded. It should involve all those who will be involved and identify:

- who and what may be harmed
- what harm could occur
- actions to be taken to minimise the risk
- how the risks and benefits will be communicated to the person we support
- when the risk assessment should be reviewed.

Consent and best interest assessment

In accordance with the Mental Capacity Act 2005, decisions regarding the use of video in staff teams must be recorded.

Where the person has the capacity to make a decision about the use of video within the staff team, consent must be sought. As part of this process, participants must be given detailed and understandable information as to the use of the recordings, and clear explanations given about the person's right to decline or withdraw their consent at any stage without fear of negative consequences.

If the person is not able to make the decision for themselves, it may be possible for a decision to be made to proceed with the video work if it is in the best interests of the person, but clear procedures must be followed, approved and documented before video work commences.

Storage and disposal

Video must be given the same status and be subject to the same safeguards as any other records and information. Video tapes, DVD and other storage devices must be clearly labelled to indicate:

- the subject matter
- the date the video was recorded
- the date by which the video must be destroyed (or reviewed)
- the name of the person responsible.

Good practice for electronic files is to ensure video files are password protected and the information above is included in the file properties.

Videotapes, DVD and disks must be stored securely and unedited, unwanted and unused footages must be deleted from memory card and sticks, computers and laptops, mobile phones and cameras as soon as practicable. Video that has been made for support and training purposes should be destroyed when they have served their purpose, and normally within six months as a maximum.

NB: Video is also an effective tool in promoting education, understanding and good practice in working with people with learning disabilities and is often used in training forums outside of the service. However, because there is no direct benefit to the individual in these circumstances, specific procedures and protocols need to be in place before this can be done for and with people who do not have the capacity to consent.

Observation

I had been worried about Bernadette for a long time. Staff who supported her felt that the extent of her intellectual and physical disabilities (which were considerable) and her age and ill health, meant that all they could do was to keep her comfortable and, as best as they could manage it, happy. I was concerned that we should try and find more ways to support her better, especially when it came to her intolerance of touch and people being near her. So I planned some time trying intensive interaction with her, and I asked for one of the team to join in and to do some video work so we could record what happened.

We followed the risk assessment and best interest procedures and though it became clear that most of the people who knew Bernadette were sceptical about the value of the exercise, they were happy to agree that it would be in her best interests to use video to record it.

In fact the video was invaluable. Looking back at what we recorded we were able to identify fragments of responsiveness that were completely missed at the time. Sharing the video with the rest of the team was very powerful. We highlighted and replayed specific moments that indicated Bernadette was briefly (so brief you could miss it), but definitely trying to interact in ways that no one had realised before. The team excitedly discussed and agreed on new approaches to interacting with Bernadette.

During the next year, the team used video repeatedly to record their interactions with Bernadette. They viewed the video in team meetings and adapted and revised their approaches in light of what they saw. As a result, Bernadette became comfortable with people sitting near her and with physical contact – as she became older and more frail, both of these became ever more important.

John, practice development advisor, United Response

Celebrating success

Effective practice leaders realise the value of celebrating success to motivate their staff. The problem is that support workers tend to take their achievements for granted. The aspects of their jobs they are very good at are generally easy for them to do as well, so they tend to dismiss them as not being worth mentioning.

A simple technique to celebrate success is to ask what went well since the last team meeting. Often staff's experience of meetings is that they focus on problems and issues and, as a result, the overall tone within the team can be rather negative. They come to meetings wondering what trouble they might be in this time and they prepare to defend themselves. Being in a defensive frame of mind, they may be economical with the truth and reluctant to discuss their practice openly. Essential communication can be lost as a result of this negative, fearful atmosphere.

By asking what went well since the last meeting, before moving onto problems, team members are given a chance to talk about their everyday successes and achievements. When you first start to use this technique, it is important to persist and probe for even small examples of things that went well. Over time, staff start to think about what achievements they will talk about in the next meeting. As a result, they are not only getting some recognition for good work, they start feeling motivated to do even more, and so have something positive to say at the next meeting. In addition, spending time talking about positive things that have happened helps to change the tone of the meeting and the overall atmosphere in the team.

Of course there are lots of other ways to celebrate success in teams including spotlighting individuals or group achievements and seeking feedback and messages from the people we support, senior managers, respected professionals or families and friends. The key is to be clear what you're celebrating so that people know which approaches and behaviours they should duplicate in the future.

Teams should celebrate their learning from failures too. If teams only celebrate successes we may inadvertently discourage creativity and positive risk taking. No amount of organisational statements and 'hype' about the importance of positive risk-taking will communicate a stronger message than one clear celebration of support or an activity which went wrong from which critical information was learned. We're not suggesting celebrating ongoing poor support or lack of planning. But it is valuable to celebrate our learning from things that didn't work out the first time, but that lay the groundwork for the development of more effective support or interesting opportunities for the people the team supports.

Identifying new opportunities

A range of techniques and tools, such as brainstorming, mapping and person-centred planning, can be used in team meetings to enable teams to come up with new ideas to develop existing activities and interactions or introduce something new for the individuals they are supporting. Coming up with fresh ideas involves teams growing opportunities, using creativity and judgement and in many cases taking their best guess at what might be successful.

Growing opportunities requires teams to look at what is happening now and use
the experience and learning from this to identify new activities, interactions and
relationships that can develop for the person being supported as a result (see **figure 2**).

Related employment
or voluntary work
opportunities

Opportunities to build on
and develop new interactions
and relationships

Similar or related
community
activities

Similar activities
or interactions at
home

Similar or related
leisure activities

Opportunities to
increase skills and
confidence

**Activity, interaction which
is successful and the
person values and enjoys**

Figure 2: Growing opportunities

Teams often struggle to think creatively because of what they perceive to be barriers in
the current practices, such as systems and risks. Judgment is about learning from the
past and avoiding mistakes. Creativity is about developing new insights and ideas for
the future, and much of people's experience at work is about judgment. Throughout
their working lives, staff are taught about the way things are and the way things should
be. They are taught to recognise standard situations and then to apply the standard
answer. The development of new insights and ideas often requires the team to
suspend judgement in order to be creative.

Creative thinking requires teams that dare to:
- be frank and honest about what works and doesn't work
- take person-centred risks
- do things differently
- take the chance that things might not work the first time.

Person-centred active support: A handbook

Ensure they are not:

■ insular or institutional

■ defensive

■ over-protective

■ constrained by system barriers.

Create interesting and new:

■ links between people, places and activities

■ opportunities and experiences

■ ways of working

■ interactions and relationships.

Don't forget to:

■ develop easy to access ways to capture, organise and communicate current thinking and ideas

■ establish clear objectives and targets to ensure ideas become a reality

■ celebrate success and continue to look for new opportunities.

Wherever possible, the person receiving support should be involved in the identifying and developing new goals. However a sense of 'alternatives' and 'possibilities' is denied to many people by the impact of their disability and curtailed experience.

The danger is that creativity is stifled for these people because no one feels able to take the decision to do things differently.

In these circumstances, teams need to be empowered to take their 'best guess', so that they can identify new opportunities for the people they support. Where this best guess is based, on a sound knowledge of the individual's likes, needs and preferences are based on observation and interpretation of their responses. Staff are well placed to figure out what new activities and interactions to try, keep doing, change or do more of in the future.

Summary

Practice leaders need to be proactive in developing effective teamwork by translating broad values statements and promises into clear expectations and clarifying each staff member's roles and responsibilities within the team.

Team meetings are an important resource as they provide a forum in which team members can review progress, raise concerns, learn from each other and celebrate success. They also give team members time and space to identify how they will continue to develop the activities and support being provided and identify new opportunities for interactions and activities. This resource needs to be carefully planned and managed to ensure meetings do not become dominated by organisational requirements and staffing issues.

Chapter 7

What is practice leadership?

'Managers stop spending most of their time in the office doing paperwork, problem-solving on the telephone or in meetings. Now they become 'practice leaders' teaching, guiding and leading their staff in providing person-centred active support to the people they serve. This means they spend most of their time with their staff, coaching them to provide good support.'

Mansell *et al*, 2005

Practice leadership is not a term that has been well defined in relation to learning disability services. It is, however, a term that is used in other work environments to describe the act of leading staff in how to do a good job.

Practice leadership is more than just coaching. It also involves the communication of clear and consistent messages regarding values, expectations and effective performance management. In the context of person-centred active support, practice leadership is defined as the development and maintenance of good staff support for the people served, through:

- **focusing** in all aspects of their work as managers, on the quality of life of the people served and how well staff support this
- **allocating** and organising staff to deliver better support, when and how the people being supported need and want it
- **coaching** staff to deliver better support by spending time with them providing feedback and modelling good practice
- **reviewing** the quality of support provided by individual staff in regular one-to-one supervision and finding ways to help staff improve it

■ **utilising** regular team meetings to review our effectiveness in supporting people to engage in meaningful activities and relationships and to find ways to improve.

Why is it important?

The development of person-centred approaches in services requires the use of a range of tools and approaches including person-centred planning, communication techniques and strategies, positive behaviour support and person-centred active support (an issue which is discussed in detail in Chapter 11). The task facing frontline managers is to turn the theory of these approaches into practice that results in high-quality person-centred support.

Successful implementation of person-centred active support is highly dependent on a manager's leadership and management of performance to:

■ redefine how staff identify and enable participation in a range of activities and relationships at home and in the community
■ recognise the value of routines in the lives of the people they are supporting, ensure opportunities to participate are offered predictably and consistently
■ develop staff's skills to support people in an enabling way, and monitor and respond to the verbal and non-verbal communications of the people they are supporting.

'An increase in scores on the Active Support Measure (leading to an increase in engagement) was strongly related to and predicted by whether or not frontline managers provided strong practice leadership. Particularly important was whether or not managers regularly observed and modelled good support to staff and whether or not they focused on engagement and person-centred active support in team meetings and supervisions.

'Working with effective practice leaders was also linked to higher levels of job satisfaction for staff and better role clarity.'

Ashman and Beadle-Brown, 2006

So this means that effective implementation and maintenance of person-centred active support requires more than the introduction of organising systems and paperwork and we have learned that telling people to do it isn't enough. Engaging with the people we support is often difficult and staff need the skills and motivation to make the rhetoric a reality. The most effective way to ensure this happens is for frontline managers to spend a large proportion of their time teaching, guiding and leading staff in provision of person-centred support.

> **Observation**
>
> Over the past five years, I have periodically visited a service for three people with complex needs in Derbyshire. I have in the past been disappointed to find that despite training and support to develop good active support, the practice in the service had not changed.
>
> In 2005, the manager at the time had provided active support training, and introduced structured daily planners. Key workers had drawn up guidelines and support plans which outlined the most effective ways for staff to support people to engage in a range of household and community activities. While the information provided was accurate and person-centred, it was clear from observing people being supported that it had not translated into real changes for the people living there. Levels of engagement remained low and staff were not skilled or confident in providing support.
>
> I knew something had changed on my last visit in 2009 because I saw people being engaged in a range of activities, from making drinks and cooking dinner to counting money and ordering taxis, and the support being provided by staff was well practiced and confidently delivered. A review of the records showed that similar daily planning systems and support information to those I observed in 2005 were in place so I was keen to find out what had made the difference.
>
> I spent some time talking to one of the staff on duty who explained, 'Yes, the plans were there before but we didn't know how to actually put them into practice. The previous manager just expected us to get on with it. I never saw her working with people and when we raised concerns or issues she wasn't able to offer any real advice or support. The new manager knows the people we support well and is around a lot to show us how to work with people. She sees what's happening each day, helps with problems and makes changes to the plans when they are needed.'
>
> Bev, practice development co-ordinator, United Response

What do practice leaders do?

Practice leaders develop a shared understanding about what is to be achieved and take an approach to leading and developing individual staff's knowledge and skills which will ensure that this is achieved.

Effective practice leaders ensure the people and teams they manage:

■ know and understand what is expected of them

- have the skills and ability to deliver on these expectations
- are supported to develop the capacity to meet these expectations
- are given feedback on their performance
- have the opportunity to discuss and contribute to individual and team aims and objectives.

Practice leaders are also aware of the impact of their own behaviour on the people they manage and are able to identify and exhibit good support practices.

Staff observation

Leading practice is important because it shows the staff in my team that supporting people to be engaged is really important here, and it lets them know that:

- I'm not asking you to do something I wouldn't or couldn't do myself
- I know the people we support, this work and how to do a good job
- I understand what's involved and what it will take
- I have skills and experience to share
- I believe this is the right thing to do
- I notice what goes on.

Linda, service manager, Derbyshire

Practice leadership is a combination of resource management (planning and organising the resources available) and performance management (developing staff's knowledge and skills) as outlined in **table 1.**

Practice leadership incorporates a number of approaches, tools and techniques which will be discussed in more detail in the other chapters in this book, including:

- establishing a culture in which individuals and the team take responsibility for the continuous improvement of support they provide and of their own skills, behaviour and contributions, as discussed in Chapter 6
- developing the right skills and motivating individuals within the team, explored in detail in Chapter 8
- increasing individual skills and confidence, through coaching, so that their job performance improves, as discussed in Chapter 9
- developing and maintaining ways to increase predictability and consistency within the staff team, as discussed in Chapters 4 and 5
- monitoring and reviewing practice and outcomes, as discussed in Chapter 10.

Table 1: Resource and performance management by practice leaders	
Practice leaders	
Plan and organise by:	**Develop staff's knowledge and skills by:**
ensuring service plans provide a description of what the service is aiming to achieve, and the steps to achieving this	promoting engagement and participation in household and community activities, and relationships as core objectives for the service and all the people it supports
identifying the resources or assistance required by the service to achieve its objectives	ensuring staff are clear about the objectives and actions required to achieve individual and service goals
providing clear and concise information about practice, including person-centred active support	ensuring staff have the knowledge and tools needed to carry out the objectives and actions required
developing and maintaining effective daily planning systems, which promote participation in a range of activities and reflects the individuals' person-centred goals	actively engaging with the team in their delivery of support, i.e. modelling, observing and feeding back
assisting staff to filter or prioritise competing demands and responsibilities	developing staff skills to support people in a consistent and enabling way
developing and maintaining effective feedback and monitoring systems	facilitating and contributing to team discussions and planning regarding person-centred support
identifying and facilitating assistance from other professionals	sharing good practice and ideas

Who are practice leaders?

Different organisational structures and job titles mean it can be difficult to identify who the primary practice leader is – team leader, service manager or location manager, but it is important that organisations are clear whose job it is, that the individual is aware that it is a key part of their role and that they do it.

While frontline managers and supervisors have the most focused and critical practice leadership role, everyone in the organisation has a part to play in leading practice. Directors and senior managers have a responsibility to create a climate in which staff know that the most important part of their job is providing effective person-centred support, in order to help people engage in meaningful activities and relationships.

Trustees or directors lead practice by:

- recognising and praising good practice
- demonstrating, through words and actions that engaging with the people we support and person-centred support is the most important part of the job.

Area and senior managers lead practice by:

- problem-solving with service managers and teams
- objective evaluation and assessment of services and support
- modelling good practice in their interactions with the people we support and staff
- planning services and resources
- recruitment of staff with appropriate values, knowledge and experience
- recognising and praising good practice
- demonstrating, through words and actions that engaging with people and person-centred support is the most important part of the job.

Practice leadership at these levels is important because it links to staff's motivation and commitment. If staff's perception of their employer's values is that despite what their mission statements and quality standards say about the importance of person-centred support, they only really care about finance or avoiding risks, for example, this will undermine their motivation to provide effective person-centred support.

Staff observation

I recently met our managing director at an open day event being held at another day service in York, where we had a conversation about what was happening at my service. He was knowledgeable about the work we were undertaking at the time and was able to discuss this and the ongoing work we do with individuals who attend the service specifically and realistically. I left the event feeling very proud of what we were achieving and knowing that the hard work and effort being put in was really being appreciated by the 'organisation'.

Some of my previous conversations with senior managers have been superficial and forced, where the person I was speaking to clearly didn't know what my service is trying to achieve, didn't understand what person-centred active support actually meant and did not have any experience of supporting people in this way. These conversations felt contrived and tokenistic and left me feeling unmotivated.

It's great to be in position where my line manager, their manager and the managing director really get it. Knowing that people higher up in an organisation know about the people we support, understand what it's like for service managers and their staff and recognise where it is really happening is one of the reasons I really like working here now.

Jayne, service manager, York

Why managers don't lead practice?

Our experience is that while we know about the importance of practice leadership, for a number of reasons managers struggle to develop this role and it is worth investigating this further.

Increasingly, managers are aware of their responsibilities for the implementation of person-centred active support, but they have to do this against a background of many other claims on their time and resources, whether generated by the needs of the people they support or in response to administrative requirements and external pressures.

At service level, managers are under pressure to respond to a variety of demands from the people they support, staff, other professionals and their employing organisation. They are required to produce evidence of their working practices in a range of areas including finance, health and safety and personnel management, and are increasingly being required to deliver training and develop external partnerships and new services.

Role strain, caused by ambiguity, conflict and overload has often been identified as a significant obstacle to practice leadership. One typical response to these concerns is for organisations to produce list of jobs and duties for managers in an attempt to make this clearer for individuals and assist them to plan their time accordingly. However, these lists often contain little concrete information about priorities and expectations and can, in fact, increase the manager's uncertainty as to what the priorities are at any given time.

Because of this uncertainty, managers may turn away from practice leadership and turn towards administrative tasks, seeking activity which is discrete and achievable, and can be routine, comforting, quiet and familiar.

That promotion to management is often seen as or leads to withdrawal from hands-on working can result in two main problems in relation to practice leadership.

- Limited contact and direct involvement in support provision can lead to managers losing touch with the people we support and current support practice, which can result in them making unrealistic demands and impractical decisions which are out of date.
- Reduced direct involvement in the provision of direct support, and modelling good practice can also result in managers losing practical and technical skills in supporting people effectively.

Both of these outcomes can lead to situations where staff are expected to comply with requests and instructions from the manager solely because of their position. This is less effective, and requires an unhealthy dependence on power and control of resources, than compliance which is based on a recognition and respect for the manager's experience and expertise.

Conversely where managers are promoted because they are good practitioners, they are often not prepared for the role of managing staff performance in a structured and systematic way. This way of working is sometimes seen as being in conflict with the often cited 'team approach' in social care settings and may be different to the individual manager's default leadership style (see Chapter 8). This can lead to managers feeling uncomfortable with, and even avoiding, the control element implicit in the manager's role, which can be particularly important in the implementation of person-centred active support.

People with learning disabilities, particularly those with profound and severe disability and challenging behaviour, required individualised and consistent support. In order for managers to identify, organise, coach and review this support, they need to have considerable skills in good practice and knowledge in all the core areas and specific areas relating to the people being supported by the service at any particular moment in time. This should include the following.

Core knowledge areas
- Learning disability
- Challenging behaviour
- Person-centred active support
- Positive behaviour support
- Communication
- Person-centred approaches
- Community building

Specific knowledge areas
- Autistic spectrum disorders
- Physical disability
- Mental health
- Dementia
- Sexuality and relationships

If managers are to provide practice leadership, those that manage them will need to ensure they have the opportunity to acquire the right level of skills and knowledge in order to successfully implement person-centred active support.

Workloads and other priorities are the most stated reasons for lack of person-centred active support implementation, but these may not be the real obstacles for some managers. Lack of management skills necessary to successfully implement changes and understanding in the principles of person-centred active support, and how it should be implemented, may be underlying issues.

Observation

For a number of years, I have been trying through bi-monthly consultation meetings with the area and service manager, to develop shift plans in a service for six people with severe learning disabilities and challenging behaviour.

Each time we met, I would explain why this was an effective way to increase predictability for the people being supported and how it would enable staff to have a more proactive approach to challenging behaviour and then we would agree what the service manager would do before the next meeting to get this started.

At the next meeting, the manager would come in (if he hadn't given apologies, which happened a lot) and immediately give an elaborate justification for not completing the agreed actions. While many of these justifications were based on fact, over time it became clear that there was a more fundamental problem.

At a recent meeting, I used the time to explore further the service manager's values and beliefs about the people living at the service and his understanding of person-centred active support. I discovered that while he had attended the relevant training courses, he believed that these things don't apply to his service, in that the people being supported there should not be 'made to do' housework and it was better to do things for people. He thought there was no point planning things in advance as the challenging behaviour would always get in the way of things happening anyway. It was clear to me then that things in the service will not change until the area manager takes some action to deal with these issues.

Bev, practice development co-ordinator, United Response

Summary

It is important for everyone involved to acknowledge the obstacles to practice leadership and to work positively to overcome them. There is often a need to identify processes and systems that can be simplified in order to give managers more time to focus on practice leadership and development, and managers need to be empowered to prioritise practice leadership as their primary objective and in some cases action will need to be taken to address conflicting values and beliefs.

> *'One cannot, however well qualified, lead from an office. Nor can one write person-centred policies or plans from ivory towers. To begin to try and apply some degree of person-centred thinking, not managers but leaders are needed by organisations.'*
>
> Osgood, 2003

The development of person-centred support requires leaders who spend most of their time with staff coaching them to provide good person-centred support. This practice leadership is vital for the successful implementation of person-centred active support and ensures the goals and aspirations of individual people we support are responded to as the priority.

Chapter 8

Skills and motivation

'... staff performance is the product of their skills and motivation. If staff are to provide effective person-centred active support, we need to ask ourselves whether staff have the skills to provide effective support and, if they do, whether staff are motivated to work this way.'

Mansell *et al*, 2005

There are two elements to achieving staff performance. The first of these is establishing and maintaining a motivational structure that facilitates person-centred approaches. In order to establish such a motivational structure, it is important to consider both the personal values and attitudes of staff as well as the motivation provided through management, including clear expectations of what is required. The second element of achieving the desired staff performance is ensuring that staff have the skills to do what is required of them. Organisations are usually better at attending to the second of these, usually by providing training for staff. However, motivation is often forgotten but critical to successful implementation. This chapter will look first at the issue of motivation and then at the issue of developing skills.

Motivation

The way staff feel about the people they support, their job and the organisation they work for determines how motivated they are.

There is a clear link between job satisfaction and motivation. Job satisfaction depends partly on tangible rewards, for example, how much the person is paid and the benefits they receive, but it also depends on the culture of the service and organisation in which they work.

Staff often feel strong fulfilment when they realise that they are making a difference in the lives of the people they support. However, because of the complex needs of some of the people we support, this realisation often requires clear communication about goals, recognition of staff's progress towards these goals and celebration when the goals are achieved. Praise and rewards therefore play an important part in managing motivation: people need to feel that their efforts will be recognised. But it is important to use praise and rewards appropriately, otherwise good practice won't be distinguished from mediocre support.

Staff observation

My manager often tells us we're doing a good job supporting the people who live here and gives praise during supervision. The problem is that she says that to everyone, including the staff that I know aren't following the shift plan or supporting people the way they want. Some of the other team members have given up on involving people in activities because they say it doesn't make any difference to the way the manager sees them anyway.

It's much easier to do things for the people we support here and I'm worried that the things we've achieved, like getting people involved in all the things going on in the house (which they really enjoy) will end up being lost and people will end up sitting in the lounge with the TV on all day, like they used to when I first came here.

Anonymous, team member, Suffolk

Celebrating achievements is an important motivation tool yet it is often forgotten. Managers can become completely focused on identifying current issues and solving problems and as a result fail to spend time identifying and celebrating successes in a meaningful way. Without ongoing acknowledgement of success, staff can become frustrated, sceptical and even cynical about the work they are doing.

Staff observation

The people we support have profound learning and physical disabilities, which means that involving people in activities is challenging. We have to think really hard about how to get things close to people and use a lot of physical support to enable people to participate.

When we first started implementing active support, the staff were keen to try and develop some new ways to do some of the household activities and

---

support people to be involved in small parts. After a couple of months, I noticed that they had stopped actively involving people and while people were still present when activities were going on, staff were no longer giving physical assistance. I discussed this with the team at length during the next team meeting and it became clear that they didn't think it was working, they couldn't see any progress.

After discussing this with John at a practice development meeting, I shared the 'presence to participation stages of involvement' with the team and we developed a way to monitor people's involvement using a more precise tool (*see chapter 12*). We started again and I made a point of recognising and getting the team to celebrate the changes that were occurring.

Recently we were reviewing a video of one of the people we support participating in cleaning his fish tank, when one of the team members said, 'look how he is smiling when his hand goes into the water – he's moved from awareness to response'. We rewound the video and watched it again, this time everyone saw it and began chatting excitedly about how all their hard work and persistence was paying off.

Gail, service manager, Gateshead

Practice leadership includes identifying goals and measures to indicate if the goals are being met or not, ongoing attention and feedback about measures towards goals, and corrective actions to redirect activities back towards achieving the goals when necessary. One of the most important tools available to practice leaders is supervision.

As part of supervision, practice leaders need to:

- ensure staff understand what is required and are committed to supporting people successfully
- develop the individual's skills and confidence in working with the people effectively
- provide effective leadership and motivate the staff member to continue to develop person-centred active support in all aspects of their work
- provide regular feedback on performance and the development of consistent approaches based on direct observation and SMART (i.e. specific, measurable, acceptable, realistic and timely) goal planning
- help the staff member to filter and prioritise competing needs and responsibilities to ensure person-centred support is the key task
- identify personal development needs in relation to practice and person-centred active support.

These are key components of good performance management which need to be happening in parallel with effective practice leadership.

Values and motivation

'An individual staff member's motivation is affected by the values they hold about the people they support and the work they do, and by their perception of the values of the organisation and their managers.'

Mansell *et al*, 2005

Values such as control, equity, participation and citizenship for people with learning disabilities are powerful motivators if they are truly integrated into the culture and practice of an organisation. They are the foundation which the organisation uses to select staff, reward and recognise good practice and guide the performance of staff. If staff see themselves as working for an organisation that values engagement and participation for all the people it supports, they are more likely to identify a wide range of opportunities to support people to participate and be creative in the way they approach this.

However, a difficulty with relying on organisational values as motivators occurs when an organisation's senior managers claim certain values and then behave in ways that are contradictory to the stated values.

Staff observation

I have worked for the same organisation for a number of years now. While the values statement has remained consistent during this time, the 'real message' about what's important changes, depending on the beliefs and priorities of the divisional area and service managers.

A couple of years ago, it became clear to me that our local managers were really only interested in developing new services and didn't want to get involved in discussions about improving the services we were already operating. This was about the time the organisational message was that we needed to continue to improve our practice by implementing person-centred active support, and we were all sent on training. When I tried to discuss this with my manager, she just said I could make any changes I felt like as long as it didn't affect the budget.

Recently a new divisional director has been appointed who has had a lot of experience and is really focused on developing person-centred approaches, including active support. Since then discussions in divisional and area

---

management meetings have become much more focused on practice issues. My manager's focus has also changed – we now discuss what is working and not working for the people we support and how effective the staff team are at providing person-centred support in every supervision. At last it feels like we're all on the same page!

Anonymous, team leader, Yorkshire

While the organisation's values and our perception of them informs staff practice, the way we support people is strongly influenced by our own personal beliefs. Staff's beliefs, attitudes and emotional responses to the people they support are intrinsically linked to the failure to implement person-centred active support.

Training and written statements or plans within services and advice from managers may not be as influential in developing staff beliefs and practice, as the informal cultures that exist within staff teams. The staff team may hold, individually or collectively, beliefs about the people they are supporting or about all people with learning disabilities which are in conflict with the organisation's. They may have adopted particular ways of supporting people which would have to be dropped if person-centred active support is implemented.

Staff emotions can be a factor when implementing person-centred active support in services where there is severe challenging behaviour. We have often found that staff in these services have developed ways of working, for example, reducing demands and interactions, which enable them to escape or avoid the negative emotions they experience as a result of challenging behaviours.

Practice leaders need to take account of staff beliefs, attitudes and emotional responses to real-life situations and develop ways of working which change, control or manage those which are in conflict. If these issues are not understood and addressed, the implementation of the person-centred active support may prove to be unsuccessful. In particular, practice leaders need to be aware that while some motivators are outside of their control, others are within their reach and need attention if the overall balance of motivation is to tip towards desired outcomes for people being supported.

Observation

During some recent training, I asked practice leaders what they thought motivated staff and which things they felt they had some control over. They came up with this list, including some things that were partially in and out of their control (indicated by shaded boxes on both sides).

We can control	Motivators	We can't control
	Having a full-staff team	▓
▓	Wanting to do well	▓
▓	Receiving constructive feedback	
▓	Helping others do well	▓
	Salary	▓
	Things going well	▓
▓	Having responsibility	▓
▓	Having fun	
	Feeling well	▓
▓	Celebrating other people's success	
▓	Recognising good work	
▓	Deadlines	▓
▓	Praise	
▓	Making a difference	
▓	Working in a pleasant environment	▓
▓	Having a plan	
▓	Developing a culture of giving and receiving gifts	

We can control	Motivators	We can't control
	Feeling valued	
	Finishing things	
	Seeing managers doing the same as them	
	Being challenged	
	Feeling involved	
	Managers being consistent	

The purpose of this exercise was to demonstrate that although practice leaders might not be in control of some motivators, for example money, personal health, etc., they had complete or partial control of a wide range of other motivators. One of the tasks of practice leaders is to work hard with the motivators they can control (to whatever extent) in order to compensate for the potential negative effect of those they can't control.

John, practice development advisor, United Response

Developing skills

'We know that in order to work with people with learning difficulties effectively both 'classroom' and practical hands-on training are essential.'

Mansell *et al*, 2005

Training can be a good way to ensure that the staff understand the goals or objectives of the service or organisation and is often necessary if individual staff are to be successful. There is a direct link between training and staff retention; staff who are involved in ongoing training feel that their employer is interested in them doing a better job, and the employer cares enough about them to make an investment in their development.

However, developing a training programme that enables staff to implement person-centred active support and improve their support skills requires some thought.

Elements of successful training include the following.

Recognition – participants are more likely to transfer their learning to the workplace when they are able to recognise that the learning is critical to them doing their job well.
Respect – respect of trainer's knowledge and experience and rapport with the trainer needs to be established.
Retention – participants must have adequate opportunities to practice what they learn to increase levels of retention.
Transference – participants must be able to transfer what they have learned in their workplace, this is more probable when the learning is new and fresh.

Training can be a means for positive change in the service, however, classroom training is not enough to create lasting change without a vital link that will help staff transfer what they learned into real-life situations. That vital link is a strong coaching programme.

Staff observation

I recently attended person-centred active support training and was excited to learn some new skills to help me think differently about the way we can help the people we support to get involved in new activities. But when I got back to work and discussed this with my supervisor, she showed no interest in what I had learned and said she was too busy to offer support. In the first few days when I came back to the service, I tried some of the new support techniques I learned on the course and encouraged the people we support to try new activities. However, after a few weeks I just went back to working the way I had before. It's a shame, I think it could have really worked here.

Anonymous, team member, Yorkshire

Training should be linked to hands-on experience and coaching to assist those who find it hard to grasp what is being taught to them in the classroom setting. Coaching (discussed in Chapter 9), when done properly, is a practice leader's most powerful tool when seeking to improve the performance of staff within their team. Effective practice leaders understand that simply sending staff to classroom training courses is not enough to make lasting changes to an individual's or team's practice. As a result, they will create training programmes which combine good classroom training with effective coaching elements. For example:

Interactive training
Classroom-based content, including group work activities is facilitated by a trainer who is experienced in providing person-centred active support. This classroom training is

closely followed by individual hands-on training by the trainer (45 to 60 minutes per person) carried out in the workplace.

Managers training and follow-up

Classroom-based training is provided by an experienced active support trainer. Following the course, participants are required to carry out a post-course assignment which requires them to practice the skills introduced during the training. The post-course work, including observation of practice, is monitored and discussed in supervision with the line manager and followed up in service monitoring and practice development meetings with area managers and practice advisors.

Team training and supervision

Modules of person-centred active support training are facilitated by the manager at a team day or during team meetings. During this training, clear actions and support practices are agreed. Implementation of the training and the agreed practices is then followed up by supervisors using observation and feedback.

Monitoring and reviewing the effectiveness of the training programme enables practice leaders to continue to develop relevant and specific person development plans for individual staff members and the team, and helps them to develop and plan future training opportunities.

Using the right leadership style to facilitate skill development

Adapted from, The Situational Leadership Model, found in Hersey P & Blanchard K (1988) *Management of organisational behaviour: Utilising human resources*. New Jersey: Prentice Hall, and Five Steps to High Performance, found in Ingham G (2007) *Motivate People: Get the best from yourself and others*. London: DK Publishing.

Whenever we learn something new, we progress through four steps.

Step 1: Unconsciously – unskilled

Step 2: Consciously – unskilled

Step 3: Consciously – skilled

Step 4: Unconsciously – unskilled

Sometimes this progress happens so quickly we are unaware of the process. At other times we are much more aware of the learning process and our feelings around it. Understanding these steps can help practice leaders understand and motivate members of their teams more effectively.

Observation

During a recent training session, a team member described her experience of working with people with learning disabilities using this framework.

When she applied for her first job supporting people in a residential home, she wasn't aware of how much she would have to learn to be able to work with people successfully, unconsciously unskilled.

During the induction, she began to realise what skills she needed to learn and realised that it was going to be a challenging and rewarding career, consciously unskilled.

After about six months in the job, after attending training and on-the-job coaching, she reached the point where she was able to support people well in a variety of situations but still needed to plan and think carefully about before and during each activity, consciously skilled.

12 months later, she felt that she can actively support people to participate in routine and new activities naturally, making the most of opportunities as they arose and supported people in ways they like and need, unconsciously skilled.

Bev, practice development co-ordinator, United Response

It is important to be aware that people will progress through the four steps at different speeds. Individual staff can be at different stages in different areas of their work, for example a team member may be unconsciously unskilled at using hand-over-hand guidance to support an individual to participate in activities, yet he could be unconsciously skilled at using objects of reference and body language to aid communication.

Operating at the unconsciously skilled level has many advantages. You can:
- multi-task
- operate fluidly and easily
- stay in your comfort zone
- remain stress free.

But it can also lead to repeating mistakes and weaknesses, particularly when the needs of the person you are supporting change over time or the expectations of your role change and develop. Complacency can develop when staff spend a lot of time operating in an unconscious way. In effect, they operate with such ease and confidence that they fail to notice anything changing around them. The 'unconsciousness' of their skill conspires to blind them to today's reality, and without noticing they become not unconsciously skilled but unconsciously unskilled (see **figure 1**).

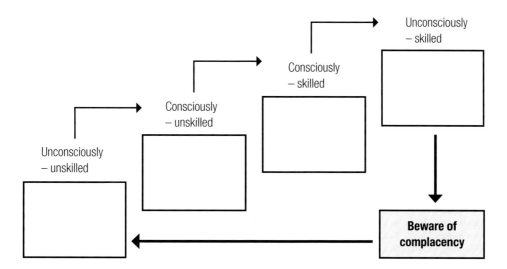

Figure 1: Four Stages to learning skills

To avoid complacency, it is important to be able to step back periodically and check that the support being provided is as effective and person centred as possible (see Chapter 10). Helping team members to understand and change support practices which do not match the current service aims and objectives or the preferences and needs of the people they are supporting requires clear direction and repeatedly practicing new support techniques.

Different leadership styles are needed at each step of the learning process, see **table 1**.

Table 1: Leadership styles	
	Leadership style
Unconsciously – unskilled	**Directing** Providing specific instructions and closely supervising outcomes
Consciously – unskilled	**Teaching** Continuing to direct and closely supervise outcomes, but also explaining decisions, soliciting suggests and supporting progress
Consciously – skilled	**Encouraging** Facilitating and supporting efforts towards successful outcomes and sharing responsibility for decision-making
Unconsciously – skilled	**Delegating** Turning over responsibility for decision-making and problem-solving

Leadership style is the way you behave when you are trying to influence the performance of others. The leadership styles, outlined above, are a combination of directive and supportive behaviours.

Directive behaviour: involves clearly telling people what to do, how to do it, where to do it and when to do it, and then closely supervising their performance.

Supportive behaviour: involves listening to people, providing support and encouragement for their efforts and then facilitating their involvement in problem-solving and decision-making.

There is no 'best' leadership style – different staff need different leadership styles depending on their understanding of what is required and their practical skills, for example, a new recruit will probably not benefit from a purely supportive style – they need to have clear information about what they need to do and how to do it in order to be successful.

A different leadership style will be needed at each step, see **figure 2**.

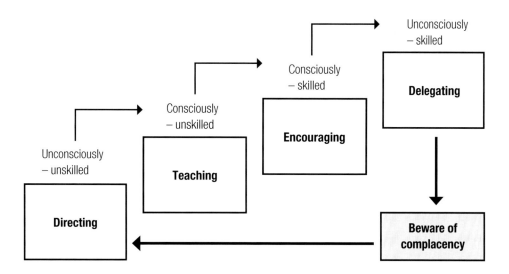

Figure 2: Matching leadership style to the four steps to learning skills

There may be barriers between steps in the learning process, where an individual is unable to develop the knowledge or skills needed in this area of their work. If this happens, it will be necessary to change back to the previous leadership style.

We have learned that most practice leaders have a default leadership style. Sometimes this is the only style they know or the only way of leading that they feel comfortable with. Crucially, our experience supports the view that practice leaders absolutely must change their style to reflect the needs of individual staff. Failure to recognise this always leads to unmotivated staff and poor services.

> ## Staff observation
> My natural style of managing is to delegate and while that has generally worked well, it was a real disaster when I was first implementing person-centred active support here a couple of years ago.
>
> While the staff team were all good caring people, they were having real difficulty seeing how and why they should change the way they had been working, long before I came along. At first, I tried to share the responsibility for decision-making about the way we would develop shift plans and I delegated planning new activities to key workers.

The next few months were a nightmare! I kept explaining what I wanted them to do, and people would say they would get on to it, but nothing changed.

I finally had to change the way I was working to be much more directive in my approach – once people could see how active support could work and how it benefits the people we support, I was able to move back to my preferred delegating style.

Anonymous, service manager, Derbyshire

Summary

Person-centred active support is a practical skill which staff need to practice in order to implement effectively, and as a result successful training programmes need to incorporate on-the-job follow-up and coaching.

Providing practical, reinforcing consequences to teams and individual staff, is an important part of the practice leader's role because motivation has an important part to play in the implementation of person-centred active support. Good practice leaders will also match their leadership style to the individual staff member's current skills and knowledge in the various aspects of their day-to-day work.

Chapter 9

Modelling and coaching

'Managers … become 'practice leaders', teaching, guiding and leading their staff in providing person-centred active support to the people they serve. This means they spend most of their time with their staff, coaching them to provide good support.'

Mansell *et al*, 2005

Chapter 7 explored practice leadership in more general terms. Effective implementation of person-centred active support requires practice leaders to use a combination of modelling, training and coaching to ensure staff have the skills and knowledge needed to support people well. This chapter will consider in detail the elements of modelling and coaching which support the development of staff skills in person-centred active support.

What is modelling?

Modelling is essentially demonstrating the desired behaviours and skills (in this case, providing good person-centred support) to staff so that they will be able to replicate them in their own work.

Clement & Bigby (2010) describe two different forms of modelling by managers as the following.

Passive modelling – using everyday opportunities to demonstrate good practice so that staff will pick up on this and learn that this is the way they are expected to behave.

Active modelling – using incidental opportunities (e.g. new activities are taking place, problems occur or poor practice is seen) during the shift or visit to the service to demonstrate how staff should be working.

Passive and active modelling are important practice leadership tools as they reinforce the message that supporting people effectively is the core objective of the service and they develop a shared understanding about how this will be achieved (see Chapter 6).

Modelling requires practice leaders to be aware of the impact of their own behaviour whenever they are supporting people and to be able to identify and exhibit good support practices at all times, which requires considerable practice skills and knowledge (see Chapter 8). This does not, however, mean every interaction or activity supported by practice leaders needs to be perfect and go exactly right every time – modelling the use of incidental opportunities to support people to engage in activities, risk taking and learning from experience are also valuable for all staff.

While modelling provides opportunities for staff to observe and imitate good practice, more focused skill development tools such as coaching and training are also required for staff to deliver person-centred active support.

What is coaching?

A coach helps people to improve their performance and motivation by empowering them to set and achieve goals and create sustainable increases in performance.

Coaching has elements of several different approaches and can often be confused with these specific approaches. Coaching is not the same as modelling, training, demonstrating, supervision, instruction or mentoring, although it might include one or more of these elements.

Here we are using the term to mean a process that happens in the work situation (not away from work like training or in supervision) between a coach and a person being coached (who we're going to call a 'coachee' as it's a handy, if inelegant abbreviation). The 'activities' typically being coached would be supporting someone in a particular activity or in a particular way, communicating effectively and identifying and acting appropriately in the early stages of increased agitation or anxiety.

While many staff have experienced being coached or coaching new staff as part of induction, this approach to developing skills and knowledge often stops once the new staff member has become familiar with the service or the people they are supporting. In many services, the only other time staff will be aware of coaching being used is as part of formal capability and disciplinary procedures and as a result coaching has often acquired a negative association.

Staff observation

When our manager came back from the practice leadership training saying she was going to introduce coaching, we were all a bit wary and suspicious. We thought it would be weird having a manager come in to show us how to support people and then watch us doing it. Some staff thought it was all a ruse to follow up on some kind of complaint and it was just a way for the manager to criticise the work we were doing.

We discussed it at the team meeting and she explained she had realised that in order to really help us get active support right, we all needed more practical help. She explained that she was going to start by having us coach her. She asked us to pick a couple of activities we thought we were really good at supporting people to do, and for a couple of volunteers to act as her coach.

I volunteered to coach her to support Barry to peel potatoes and we booked a coaching session in the next week. I started off by explaining the support plan to her before we went into the dining room where Barry was helping to cook the dinner. I supported Barry to peel half the potatoes while she watched me, she then asked me a couple of questions about the hand-over-hand support I was giving Barry before we swapped over. I watched them finish off the potatoes and we thanked Barry and went into the office so I could give her some feedback. She did pretty well but I reminded her that Barry doesn't understand much verbal communication and that she was probably using too many words and talking about other things, which was distracting him when he was trying to concentrate. She thanked me and we agreed to have another coaching session in a couple of days time.

Over the next couple of days, the team asked me what it was like and I explained that it was not as scary as it sounded. Coaching has now become a regular part of everyone's supervision and happens regularly. It's not done because someone's in trouble, it's one of the ways we share good practice and solve problems together.

Susan, team member, Derbyshire

As discussed in Chapter 8, coaching has been demonstrated to be much more effective in improving person-centred active support than training alone. Good coaching practice promotes open communication and improves working relationships by showing how everyone contributes and learns from each other. Coaches can increase motivation by asking the right questions and listening to what people have to say, encouraging them to embrace change and learn from mistakes they make.

Creating a supportive coaching environment will empower individuals so that they are open and receptive to developmental feedback and keen to take action to improve their skills. It is also our experience that using coaching proactively can reduce the need for capability and disciplinary procedures.

A great deal of information about the staff team and service can come from coaching. Themes, common issues, descriptions of leadership or service culture will inevitably emerge from coaching conversations and can be used to help the service learn and continue to improve the support it provides.

The best way to help shape up skilled support is for practice leaders to coach staff, spending time with each member of the team, observing their practice, giving feedback on things they are doing well and making suggestions for how they could do better. Successful coaching takes more than being able to do the job well. Coaches need to learn and practice the ability to share knowledge and skills effectively. Coaching is a cycle of demonstration, discussion, observation and feedback, which is repeated until performance is satisfactory or some other process is required, see **figure 1**.

Steps to successful coaching

1. **Focus**
    - Establish rapport
    - Communicate your expectations
    - Find out what the staff member can do

Then

2. **Explain and demonstrate**
    - Explain the steps of the task
    - Explain why they are important
    - Demonstrate them

3. **Observe**
    - Staff member explains and demonstrates what the coach demonstrated in step 2

4. **Feedback**
    - Coach staff and member discuss performance in step 3

5. **Repeat if necessary**

Figure 1: Steps to successful coaching

1. Focus

Establishing rapport is at the centre of effective coaching. The coach needs to devote their full attention to the 'coachee' during the coaching session and actively listen and understand their point of view.

Because the primary objective for coaching is to develop staff skills and knowledge, the coach must be able to accurately assess the staff members' strengths and development needs, develop reasonable performance expectations, and to develop a mutually agreed-upon coaching plan.

2. Explain and demonstrate

Having identified the coaching activity or support techniques, the next step is for the coach to explain the steps of the activity or the support to be provided, and why they are important (support plans or interaction profiles could be used as the basis for this). The coach will then demonstrate how to do this effectively.

3. Observe

Next the coach needs to observe the 'coachee' doing the same or similar thing.

Sometimes it is possible to do this in one session but, because the person being supported has already completed the activity with the coach, it may be necessary to wait and plan for another opportunity when the person being supported wants or needs to do the activity again.

During the observation, it can be helpful to note any 'successful strategies' such as examples of things the 'coachee' did well that can be fed back after the observation and 'helpful hints' – areas to work on that need improving, or ideas on how to provide better support, using the headings presented in the PCAS training pack (worksheet 3.4), which are as follows:

- Did the staff member prepare the situation so that the flow of activity was maintained?
- Did he or she present the opportunity well?
- Did he or she provide graded assistance?
- Did he or she enable the person to experience success?
- Did he or she provide support with a positive, helpful style?

4. Feedback

Having observed the coachee, the coach needs to clearly describe the coachee's practice and identify specific ways for further performance improvement.

BOOST feedback model

Balanced – include both good and constructive points.

Observed – only give examples of what you have seen the person say or do.

Objective – feedback should be factual and not attach on someone's personality. It should focus on actions and not your feelings about the person.

Specific – always use specific examples.

Timely – feedback should be given as close to the event as possible. This will ensure accuracy.

Feedback must be based on observed facts about behaviour in order to prevent people taking the message personally and becoming resistant. Once the feedback has been given, the coach should listen to what the coachee has to say before asking them what they think they could do in future to improve the support they provide, or making suggestions themselves.

It is important to note that different feedback styles work for different people. Coaches need to take into account the learning steps and leadership styles discussed in Chapter 8 and identify which step relates best to the coachee, the activity or task, and match their feedback style to the leadership style that is most effective. A questioning approach when feeding back can work well with a 'consciously skilled' member of staff but will not be successful with one who is 'consciously unskilled'. When coaching a 'complacent' and therefore 'unconsciously unskilled' member of staff, asking the person can result in defensive discussions about why their well-practiced support is right – a more direct approach to what is required and how their observed performance met or did not meet the required standard is normally required, at least initially.

5. Repeat if necessary

Steps 2, 3 and 4 are then repeated until either the coachee demonstrates the expected performance or until it is not reasonable to continue – in which case other performance management strategies, such as capability or disciplinary procedures will need to be pursued.

Once the required performance has been achieved, the coach needs to ensure the coachee has a good understanding of the skills learned and how this learning can be utilised in other activities or in support situations. The coach and coachee should identify and move onto new coaching targets.

Staff observation

I had been working here for about three months and felt confident about supporting most of the people who live here, but was finding it really difficult to support Tony to engage in activities. His key worker had put together a support profile which helped me to understand what sort of activities he liked doing and how to prepare them, which helped a lot, but I just couldn't seem to get my support during the activities right.

I explained this to Mary, my supervisor, who organised some coaching sessions to help me. We started off by spending some time talking about the support profile and discussing what good support looks like for Tony. Mary then arranged to come in and work with me on four separate occasions over the following week. Each time she came in, we identified the activities that Tony wanted to do. Mary then explained how she was going to support Tony and what things I should look out for. I would watch her support him initially and then we would swap over and she would watch me until the activity was finished. Next Mary sat down with me to tell me the things I had done well and explain how I could do it better next time.

The first thing we identified was that I was going too fast. Tony needed more time to process the information and instructions I was giving him. Over the next few coaching sessions, I learned how to slow things down and wait until Tony was ready to do the next step. Mary then pointed out that I was using too many verbal prompts and she showed me how I could use objects and gestures to help Tony see what he needed to do next.

It was because Mary showed me how to support Tony in a range of activities that I was able to see how these principles apply in all my interactions with him, and as a result, I now feel confident and comfortable supporting him at home and when we are out in the community.

Helena, team member, Suffolk

Who should be a coach?

Coaching is generally seen as the responsibility of line managers but it can also be delivered by external coaches, or by skilled staff coaching each other.

Managers

Managers as practice leaders have a direct responsibility to develop the skills, knowledge and confidence of their staff and so are natural candidates. As well as providing opportunities to work closely with staff, their direct involvement models this way of working for others in the team.

Supervisors

Supervision is a process in which one worker is given responsibility to work with another in order to achieve agreed professional, personal and service goals. Where these goals are centred on support practices, there is a clear fit with the coaching role. Integrating coaching into supervision ensures that supervision discussions, action plans and personal development planning are grounded in reality.

Other team members

Individuals in teams have a variety of gifts and strengths which can be shared. Where team members are particularly skilled at supporting people in a range of activities and relationships, there can be opportunities to develop these individuals as coaches.

External consultant or trainers

Occasionally services have access to external consultants, trainers or other professionals who have experience in providing person-centred active support who can also provide coaching to individuals within the team. This may be in the form of hands-on training as part of a training programme or as follow-up to an assessment or consultation process.

While it is possible for a range of people to coach person-centred active support, our experience suggests these approaches are not as effective as when coaching is part of a line management relationship.

Developing coaching skills

Coaching is an effective way of developing practice skills. However, coaching is only effective if coaches understand the coaching process, understand their role within the process and can demonstrate the skills associated with effective coaching, which include:

- recognising and creating opportunities for coaching
- effective listening
- building rapport
- giving feedback
- goal setting, questioning
- dealing with conflict

Person-centred active support: A handbook   © Pavilion Publishing (Brighton) Ltd 2010

- reflection on strengths and development needs
- individual action planning.

Real life practice is the only way to become an effective coach but there are also other tools which can be used to help develop coaching skills. Using a variety of media including role plays, simulations, experiential exercises and videos can enable practice in some or all coaching skills within a realistic scenario.

We have found that video has been particularly useful during coach training and supervisions as it gives participants opportunities to practice identifying poor support practices, and prioritising feedback points, practice giving feedback which matches learning steps, and to explore common obstacles and challenges that occur in a coaching situation and how to address them.

Supervising coaching

Coaching good practice in supporting people to be engaged in a range of activities and relationships can be a challenging and sometimes lonely activity and as a result, coaches can benefit from structured opportunities to reflect on their practice. Such opportunities, in one-to-one or group sessions, can help coaches to develop their skills as well as provide them with support. It can also be an important quality check and a source of wider learning about issues being addressed in coaching sessions.

Without supervision, it's hard to be sure that coaching standards are good and that coaches are properly trained and supported in their roles.

The potential benefits of coaching supervision are easily identified as:

- developing coaching capacity
- assuring the quality of coaching
- sharing good practice and ideas
- improving collaborative working
- identifying wider themes and issues
- monitoring of coaching quality and minimising the risk of unethical or unprofessional practice.

Staff observation

As part of implementing person-centred active support in our area a couple of years ago, all the senior support workers who were doing supervisions were trained as coaches. Since then, I have been including regular coaching

---

sessions in my supervisions with the two support workers I supervise. It was nerve racking at first, I think I'm pretty good at supporting the guys who live here but having to demonstrate the right way to do things and then feedback to the others was a new experience for me.

My manager has been very supportive and we regularly talk about this part of my job in my supervision, but the thing that has helped me most is the group supervisions for coaches, which we have every two months. During these meetings, all the coaches from the area get together to share experiences and feelings about coaching.

We generally start the meeting with a round of what's working and what's not working for us as coaches. Then one person shares a current coaching situation or issue and the other coaches ask questions and share ideas and suggestions. We usually have time to split into groups of two or three to talk about individual issues or concerns we may have. We always finish up by recording any common themes or issues, and passing them onto the area manager.

Meeting with other coaches has helped me to build up my confidence and I've learned a lot more about coaching along the way.

Jackie, senior support worker, Nottingham

Creating a coaching environment

A coaching environment is one where coaching is the predominant style of managing and working together, and where commitment to improving the support being provided is embedded in a parallel commitment to improving the skills, knowledge and confidence of the staff team. It is an environment in which not only formal coaching occurs but also where most people use coaching behaviours as a means of managing, influencing and communicating with each other.

The first step in creating a coaching environment is to increase the acceptance of coaching. Practice leaders and supervisors should be the first people to learn about and experience coaching, simply because once they have discovered how successful it can be they will be keen to see it cascade throughout the team. It is important to remember that for some staff, coaching will be associated with capability or disciplinary procedures and to be prepared for reluctance or resistance which may result. Initial resistance can normally be overcome by explaining the benefits, enabling individual staff to understand how coaching can help and motivate them as well as improve the quality of support individuals receive.

The second step is to develop a clear coaching methodology. If it is to become an accepted part of the way the team works, coaching must demonstrate clear outcomes. It should be related to practical issues and goals for the people we support and the staff team. Coaches and participants must agree clear success criteria, and it must be a process where feedback is provided as a matter of course.

Developing a coaching environment has distinct phases, starting with these initial steps through to the development of critical mass and a period of self-sustaining growth. The challenge is to develop and embed models and practices in coaching so that it can provide the maximum support and benefit for the people being supported, staff and coaches.

Summary

Modelling and coaching have an important role in the implementation of person-centred active support and have a significant impact on the skills and motivation (and thereby, robustness) of the staff team. While modelling is often seen as a natural and effective way to share and demonstrate good practice, it is not a robust or consistent tool for changing entrenched approaches to support.

Coaching is a powerful staff development tool which practice leaders need to utilise and model routinely. While the primary responsibility for coaching may rest with the manager, it can also be effectively delivered by other staff within the team – an approach which can have advantages when it is linked to supervision systems and can help to develop a coaching environment.

Chapter 10

Monitoring and reviewing

'Improving the quality of support involves looking at what people are really doing, rather than relying on plans, records or other paperwork. This means focusing on activities and relationships as the measure of quality…'

Mansell *et al*, 2005

Reviewing the implementation and impact of person-centred active support serves a number of important functions for the service and the people it supports. It helps us to identify what is important to each person and how well the support we are providing matches their needs and preferences. Identifying the elements of our support which are working and not working, enables us to continue to utilise and develop successful support approaches and adjust or revise elements of our support that are ineffective.

Reviewing also provides information about the frequency and quality of the activities and relationships the individuals being supported are involved in, which enables us to celebrate successes and also provides early warnings about difficulties or reductions in the quality of the support or service being provided.

Services often do a lot of recording and monitoring but are not effective at reviewing and acting on what has been learned. Because the terms 'recording', 'monitoring' and 'reviewed' are often used interchangeably, it may be helpful to define these terms before looking at each one in more detail.

Recording – the act of making a record, a body of information or statistics gathered over time – something that acts as evidence

Monitoring – to check something at regular intervals in order to find out how it is progressing or developing

Reviewing – to look at something critically; to examine something to make sure it is adequate, accurate or correct; to consider something again; to check something again

Recording and monitoring are important steps in the overall reviewing process (see **figure 1**). Crucially, if they are to have any real value, they must lead to action.

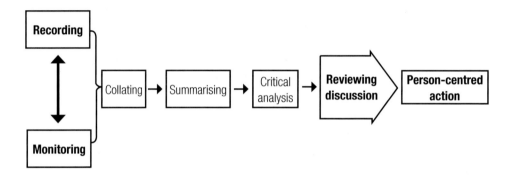

Figure 1: The reviewing process

Recording should only be done if it has a clear and current purpose. One of the most common complaints from staff, often justifiably, is the unrealistic amount of recording they are required to complete for no apparent reason.

Observation

When visiting Simon's service, I was shown into the sleeping-in room for a quick chat with the team member on duty. I asked how they recorded what activities Simon was successfully involved in, and the team member looked at me and then looked under the desk where a two foot pile of A4 paper was partially contained in a cardboard box. The staff member explained that these were daily 'keeping track' records. He said, 'We fill them in every day and after they've sat in the file for a couple of weeks, we transfer them down there'.

I asked if anybody went through them to find out what was working and what might need changing. He looked at me again, laughed and said, 'No, they just sit in that pile there. We have to fill them in because the manager has told us to, but it's pretty meaningless really. To be honest, I think most staff have given up a bit – I think they just tick the boxes at the end of the shift without thinking about it.'

John, practice development advisor, United Response

Tips for effective recording

- Ensure the people collecting and recording the information understand what the information is used for. If staff understand why they are recording information, they are more likely to do so accurately.
- Give feedback on the results to the people who recorded the information in a meaningful and timely manner.
- Make sure those recording the information have clear and consistent guidelines on how to go about it.
- Write down what forms are used, when and how they should be filled in, and what the information is used for. This means that knowledge does not get lost in one person's head and it enables teams to see when something is no longer required.
- Store the information appropriately.
- Check that you are not collecting the same piece of information more than once.

Quantitative and qualitative recording

Records can provide quantitative and qualitative information. Quantitative monitoring tools (such as participation records) are those which focus on numbers and frequencies rather than meaning and experience. Quantitative records provide information that is easy to analyse statistically and fairly reliable but do not provide in-depth descriptions.

Qualitative monitoring tools are ways of collecting data concerned with describing details of how support was provided and how the person responded, rather than providing statistical information. Qualitative methods (such as activity records and learning logs) provide more in-depth and rich descriptions of what happened.

Both quantitative and qualitative information are needed in order to effectively review the implementation of person-centred active support and continue to improve our practice. Effective reviewing systems have a combination of both, which ensures that we are able to produce numerical measurements which are backed up by and enriched by detailed information about effective support or lessons learned.

Examples of recording

Participation records

Adapted from, Jones *et al* (1997) *Active Support Trainers Manual*. Cardiff: Welsh Centre for Learning Disabilities Applied Research Unit.

Each person we support has a personalised record of activities they regularly participate in. Throughout the day, the person or the staff member supporting them ticks the activities the person has been involved in. The standardised 'keeping track' forms often used as part of setting up active support contains 10 categories. But the forms should be individualised or adapted to make them more person centred and accessible for the individual being supported.

Forms are tallied up each week and transferred to a participation summary which gives an overview of the activities the person has participated in over a 6–12 month period. This form of recording shows the range of opportunities available to the person and the extent to which people are engaged and is useful to monitor whether the level of opportunities and engagement is increasing, deceasing or being maintained over time.

Learning logs

(Smull *et al*, 2005)
Learning logs are used in some services to replace traditional notes or records by recording:

- what the person did
- who was there
- what was learned about what worked well
- what was learned about what didn't work.

They work particularly well where people are trying new activities or experiences. Information from the learning log is used to identify the parts of the activity or elements of the support received that need to stay the same and the things that need to change.

Support and teaching plan records

Records of the implementation of individual support and teaching plans (discussed in Chapter 5), can also be a source of quantitative and qualitative information.

Sampling

Services routinely record some information about individual's activities and participation for long periods of time, however, this information does not always provide an accurate picture. This is because inconsistencies arise over a period of time, particularly when staff are not aware of how and why information is being collected or information is not utilised for long periods. There may be inconsistent reporting between staff (e.g. some staff or shifts may be somewhat lax in filling in forms) and changes in reporting systems, priorities or management focus which can lead to increased or decreased recording (e.g. managers or staff may have had a drive at a particular point in time to ensure that all participation summaries were completed).

Observation

I did some work with a team which was struggling with Gail's behaviour. She had recently moved into one of a number of independent flats, but found various aspects of her new living arrangements difficult. I suggested that the team record the number of times she became distressed as well as how often other things happened that they thought might be significant. We drew up a tally record for them to use. When I asked about how they were going to collate and analyse the records, they became uncertain particularly about the time that would be involved. So I suggested that they send the charts to me at the end of each month for analysis.

Over the next few months, I was able to identify some possible relationships between Gail's behaviour and other events in her life. However, I was struck by a sudden increase in the frequency of what the staff saw as challenging behaviour, in the last few days of each month's records. It rose from one or two episodes a day to eight or nine.

I rang the manager to find out what could account for this sharp increase and she did some investigating and reported back that there was nothing of note. When she asked staff, they said that Gail's behaviour was the same as normal.

We agreed that the most likely explanation for the increased recording of challenging behaviour was that staff were conscious about putting the records in the post, and were either more diligent in recording or just took more note of the behaviour.

John, practice development advisor, United Response

Monitoring

We need to be able to demonstrate the effectiveness and value of the support we provide but if we try to do this by only asking staff to fill in forms, we run the risk of inadvertently focusing attention on paperwork rather than on what is really happening in the relationship between staff and the people they support.

Simply recording what is happening is not enough. Though it is sometimes viewed as an outcome in itself, recording must have a purpose and enable monitoring as part of a wider reviewing system. Monitoring utilises a number of tools and approaches to periodically check how things are progressing. It helps us understand what is going well and what is going wrong and to discover what individuals do or don't do, rather than what they say they are doing.

There are a number of tools and approaches to periodically check how things are progressing. Here we will focus on observation.

Direct observation

'You need to focus on what is really happening, not on what records or paperwork says, or on what you think might be happening. To be really helpful to you and your colleagues, you need a fresh pair of eyes to look at the extent of engagement in meaningful activity and relationships and the quality of person-centred active support.'

Mansell *et al*, 2005

Observation is an important means of monitoring the implementation of person-centred active support and its impact on the lives of the people being supported. It is also a valuable tool for cross-checking written records and reports. While observations are typically carried out by a person in the environment where support and activities occur, video can be used as long as it has been appropriately agreed and risk assessed (as discussed in Chapter 6).

While it is possible to pick up some of this information while working on shift, or when you are in the service on other business, a lot is missed because you are supporting people or carrying out specific administrative activities (e.g. completing audit or health and safety checks, writing reports, checking petty cash). Specific observation, where your only job is to look at what is happening and how those in the environment respond, enables you to see much more. Even short observations of this kind can produce detailed and valuable information.

Staff observation

I was recently required to carry out an observation of a team member as part of my person-centred active support training. I was sceptical about the value of this and tried to argue that I do this all the time when I am in the service – and there was no need to be so formal or clinical about it. I thought about the people we support and how staff would find it difficult to have me standing in the corner watching.

Boy was I wrong! I can't believe how much I saw. I was able to really see the detail of how the team member provided support and was able to pick up on a wide range of non-verbal responses from the person being supported, which would have been easily missed if I had been providing support or doing something else at the same time. I was able to give the team member detailed feedback on what worked during the activity and made a couple of suggestions

---

for how she could improve her support. I was also able to feedback to the team some suggestions for how we could develop the activity to provide more opportunities for the person being supported to participate successfully.

Since this first observation, I have started to plan in two to three observations each week and have now observed and given feedback to every member of staff on the team. Now that everyone has experienced this for themselves, I am working with the senior support workers to develop their observation skills. My plan is to develop observation as part of the supervision process, so that staff get real feedback about their work at each supervision meeting.

Jackie, service manager, Manchester

In order to carry effective observations, you need to spend time looking at the detail of what goes on and to do this with an open mind and fresh eyes. While this sounds obvious, being impartial and analytical about what you see can be difficult when you are familiar with current practices or when you have a vested interest in things being right. It is important to be aware of your biases so that you do not suppress information you find that does not fit with your views and beliefs about the service, and support you and your team are providing.

Observation

During an observation in a supported living service for two people, I was aware that the kitchen, laundry, pantry and office doors were all locked at various times. The keys were hanging outside the office door and one of the people being supported routinely retrieved them and let himself into these areas. I was puzzled as I had met the people being supported before and wasn't aware of any risks or challenging behaviour that would require this kind of intervention.

During my feedback, I asked the area manager about this. She looked surprised and said, 'Are we still doing that? I can't believe I hadn't noticed – I visit the house regularly and hadn't even seen it'. She went on to explain that this had become common practice three or four years ago in response to the risks posed by another person living there, but he had moved out two years ago.

Bev, practice development co-ordinator, United Response

Using a checklist during observations can be helpful as it reminds you of things to look out for or enables you to focus on particular issues and practices. Observation checklists can focus on different aspects of the environment, activities and support and the following examples have been included in the appendices.

- The practice hit list (Appendix 2) outlines a range of common indicators of good or bad practice and requires the observer to record why each is or is not an issue.
- The observation checklist (Appendix 3) utilises working and not working headings to examine environment, routines and predictability, interactions with staff and other people we support, staff skills and confidence and communication.
- The observation of engagement and quality of staff support includes a brief measure of engagement, quality of staff support and practice leadership (Appendix 4) and a guide to its use (Appendix 5).

Observation tips

Confident, unobtrusive observers will rapidly blend into the background and need not be a critical imposition in the lives of the people being observed. A few tips we've picked up during the hundreds of observations we have been involved in, during our research, are outlined in Appendix 6.

Consent

If you are observing somewhere which is not your normal workplace, consent should be sought from the people we support prior to the observation using a simple written information sheet. Where an individual's capacity to consent is uncertain, a risk and benefit analysis should be carried out and the decision recorded. It is also important to remember that consent is not permanent and therefore if during the observation the people we support express or show signs of being unhappy or uncomfortable as a result of your presence, this needs to be taken as evidence of withdrawal of consent and the observation stopped immediately. An example of a risk and benefit analysis can be found in Appendix 7.

Collating information

Collation is the process of bringing the records together so we can see what information we have. Once we have all the records in one place, we can compare information from different sources so we can verify that the information fits together, identify any information gaps, integrate information from different sources and arrange the information in ways that will make summarising easier.

Three steps to collating information from different sources are as follows.

1. Identify and gather relevant records and reports.
2. Examine the information received and identify any gaps.
3. Amalgamate information from different sources that relate to interesting or important issues or events.

Summarising

The requirement for services to produce evidence of their work with the people they support, over a long period of time, often results in copious record keeping. But these records are of little value when the information they contain is not accessible.

Effective techniques to summarise the information gathered are essential for a number of reasons.

- They help us to make sense and get a feel for the information we have.
- They help us to identify the learning or issues we want to take forward in the reviewing process.
- They make it easier to pass on the learning from the information gathered to others, without them needing to review all the information.

Ways to summarise the information

Using total scores

The simplest way to summarise quantitative information that has been collected is to decide the basic time unit (day, week, month) and then add up the total score of each unit (e.g. the frequency of participation in household and community activities, the duration of involvement in activities, the number of times consistency of support or flow of activity made a difference).

Using percentage scores

The number of total instances of engagement can be condensed by calculating the percentage for a series of scores and using a single measure to monitor progress. This may be useful when the number of daily records is large and is essential if records that contribute to the total score have been missed out or lost. For example, if monitoring was set up in terms of weekly totals for activities planned on the shift plan, and some day records were not kept or a daily recording sheet is missing, then the total for that month could not be compared to the totals from other months when records were available for every day.

The percentage is calculated using the following formula:

$$\frac{\text{Total score}}{\text{Number of units from which the total score is derived}} \times 100$$

In the following example, the number of times Mary participated in planned activities was divided by the number of times activities were planned on shift over the last month.

Mary was actively engaged in 75 of the 122 opportunities planned on the shift planner this month (75/122 x 100), which resulted in a percentage score for successful participation in planned activities of 62%.

Further analysis was carried out to indicate where changes to activities had occurred. Records showed that nine out of the 122 planned opportunities had been cancelled because of staff absence reducing numbers on shift, so we were able to report that 7% of the planned opportunities were cancelled due to staffing shortages.

In the same month we also found that Mary only participated in one activity of the three activities planning on the days when she was being supported by agency staff.

In our summary for the staff team, anecdotal information was also added to highlight significant issues which needed to be considered when reviewing the information from the last month, e.g. the supermarket where Mary does her bi-weekly shopping is currently being refurbished and the fact that Mary was unwell for one week this month.

Verbal and written summaries can be lengthy and difficult to interpret. Because our records or feedback often contain lots of information, it can be difficult to get an overview, notice changes and identify trends. Converting all or some of the information gathered into graphs, charts or other visual summaries can help us to manage the information so we can identify what needs to happen next.

Visual summaries, such as graphs and charts can help us to:
- see change over time at a single glance
- share information in a clear and accessible way
- make information gathering interesting
- see relationships and trends that are missed when we look at individual recording sheets
- develop an accurate and permanent record of progress that can be updated regularly.

Presenting information in a more visual way can be motivating for staff and the people we support because people are able to see and celebrate the achievements and progress (see **figure 2**). Having a permanent reminder of achievements or presenting a colourful and attractive chart or graph at a review can be more meaningful to the people we support than a lengthy written or verbal report.

Mary's participation information Jan 2010

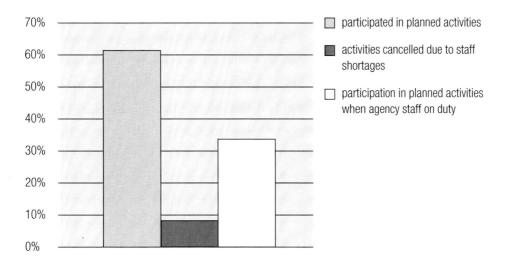

Figure 2: Mary's participation graph

Incorporating qualitative information

While quantitative data is vital when developing objective information to review, it is frequently beneficial to summarise qualitative records. Stories and other anecdotal information usually promote deeper understanding of the issues involved and can be used to illustrate what's actually going on in a way that staff and others can relate to more readily.

By itself, a report about how Mary responded to one particular agency worker's attempts to support her in an activity is limited in its relevance (perhaps only to performance discussions with that worker). In other circumstances than those described above, it might be wholly unrepresentative, and frequent circulation of the story would lead to adverse and unfair reputations for Mary or the worker. However, if as in this case, it does seem to represent a universal concern, the story could be used to illustrate the sorts of issues involved and to help staff focus on the matter under discussion.

However, summarising large amounts of qualitative data is unwieldy and time consuming – it seems unlikely that substantial use of qualitative data analysis techniques (e.g. see Miles and Huberman, 1994) will bring proportionate benefit to the implementation of person-centred active support. We would suggest that marshalling qualitative information to illustrate and deepen the learning from quantitative data represents its effective use.

Critical analysis

Analysing, reflecting upon and judging the information gathered, can be the most difficult part of the review process but is also the most important. Without this, teams will only identify approaches to specific activities and identify solutions to the difficulties in particular circumstances. Specific problem-solving of this kind, while often necessary, is not sufficient to allow teams to understand the wider implications of the information they have gathered over time.

Observation

Sometimes, when I train staff, I use exercises that ask them to analyse information. Generally, they discuss the information and then start to analyse. Frequently, however, they end up with a list that condenses the information they've been given, but they don't look behind it for unifying themes. So they might list the different supermarkets that the person seems not to like without making the link to common issues (like lighting, noise, crowds, etc.) that were the common features of the person's visits to supermarkets.

John, practice development advisor, United Response

Critical analysis requires the person viewing the summarised information to consider and evaluate the summary and factors involved, to ask themselves what this information tells them about the characteristics, needs or preferences of the person being supported.

The person analysing the information needs to be critical and to base their judgement on experience gained by working with and knowing the person being supported well, on their own knowledge and observations, and on a balanced understanding of what constitutes good person-centred support. It should always be approached in a critical manner; those looking at the information shouldn't take everything at face value, and not just stick with what is 'known' about the person being supported.

Identifying root causes – the 'five whys' strategy

The five whys is a simple problem-solving technique that helps us to get to the root of a problem quickly. It is easy to apply and involves looking at what works and what doesn't work for people by asking 'Why?' and 'What causes this?'

Very often the answer to the first 'Why?' will prompt another 'Why?' and the answer to the second will prompt another and so on.

Using the example of Mary's reduced involvement in activities when agency staff are supporting her, we can apply the 'five whys' strategy.

Q. Why does Mary only participate in one activity out of the three activities planned on days when she is being supported by agency staff?
A. Because agency staff don't provide the support Mary likes and needs.

Q. Why do the agency staff fail to provide support to Mary in a way that she likes and needs?
A. Because agency staff don't know how she likes and needs to be supported.

Q. Why do the agency staff not know how Mary likes to be supported?
A. Because they have not read Mary's support profile.

Q. Why have the agency staff not read Mary's support profile?
A. Because reading this information is not part of the normal handover procedure.

Q. Why isn't reading people's support profile part of the handover procedure for agency staff?
A. Because we don't have an agreed handover procedure for agency staff which includes giving them the information they need to support people well.

Identifying underlying themes, needs or preferences

As previously described, when looking at records we often come up with solutions or ways to change or improve our support for the specific situation or set of circumstances described. However, we are not good at generalising this learning more broadly so that the principles can be applied in other areas of the person's life.

Many of the individual activities and situations we record contain some type of lesson or message that the person we support is conveying through their responses. Recognising this helps us to develop a better understanding of the preferences and needs which are important to or for the individual, and to identify themes which can be used to help us plan and support people more effectively in a variety of situations and circumstances.

These themes may not be that obvious at first, and it may take time for some staff to develop this way of looking at information. The key is to look at specific instances or situations, but then paying attention to key events, feedback and changes in the person's actions or responses to try to see how the lessons or messages relate to the person generally.

For the people we support, there are particular factors which make support more or less likely to be successful and which should be considered when identifying themes. These include:

- continuity
- predictability
- misjudged comprehension
- unrealistic expectations
- long periods of disengagement
- not waiting
- not recognising institutional experience.

So exploring Mary's experience, we can detect a possible theme beneath the individual events. She seems to be poorly served when supported by people who don't know her well, and when activities are changed, this would suggest that successful support for Mary needs to be predictable, and when it is not, her participation will reduce. This is a theme with universal application to take to the next stage of the reviewing process.

Once root causes or underlying themes have been identified, they can be presented to others involved in the reviewing discussion for consideration.

The reviewing discussion

Once recording and monitoring information has been collated, summarised and critically analysed, we are ready to discuss what has been identified and learned, and decide what actions need to be taken.

These discussions can happen in a range of forums (e.g. person-centred review meetings and meetings with professionals) but should routinely occur in supervisions, to review how staff are doing, and team meetings to review the extent of engagement in meaningful activities and relationships by the people using the service and to identify ways to improve the support being provided.

Tips for effective reviewing discussions

■ Involve the whole staff team and where possible the people we support and those close to them in reviewing discussions to ensure their views are included.

■ Create a positive and productive environment for reviewing discussions which take account of the needs of all those involved.

■ Make sure that participants get the information they need in a timely fashion, so they are able to make and communicate suggestions about what action could and should be taken in the future.

Person-centred action

Effective reviewing can lead to clear and concise information about the people we support and our practice, which can help us to continue to develop successful support systems and strategies. However, the effort is wasted if it doesn't result in person-centred action.

In order to review effectively, teams need to:

■ **look** closely at the information

■ **discuss** the information with others (the individuals being supported, staff, other professionals, family and friends)

■ **learn** from the information and discussion what needs to change and what needs to stay the same as well as the new things to do or try

■ and then take action!

Summary

Reviewing the implementation of person-centred active support serves a number of important functions for the service and the people it supports. While there are often high levels of recording and monitoring, effective reviewing which results in person-centred action doesn't happen often enough. The development of effective reviewing systems, which include recording, monitoring, collating, summarising, critical analysis and reviewing discussions, requires conscious effort on the part of practice leaders and teams.

Chapter 11

Linking person-centred active support

'To make progress means turning person-centred plans into person-centred action. Some of this may be about changing where people live or work, or what kind of funding they received. But for people with significant disabilities, person-centred action will always entail providing direct practical support to the individual to help them make the most of the opportunities available in their life. This kind of help (which might include 'person-centred active support' or 'positive behaviour support' or 'total communication') is essential to help people get what they want in reality.'

Mansell *et al*, 2005

Integrating approaches

Supporting people with learning disabilities can seem complex, and to enable improvements to the support people receive and to their quality of life, a range of approaches and tools have been developed including the following.

Person-centred active support

Recognises that most people using services will need some practical help to engage in meaningful activity and relationships, and:

■ involves providing enough help to enable people to participate successfully in meaningful activities and relationships so that people gain more control over their lives, gain more independence and become more included as a valued member of their community

- irrespective of the degree of learning disability or the presence of extra problems such as challenging behaviour.

Communication strategies

Recognise that to listen to people, we have to know how each person communicates, and be able to communicate with them and use a range of tools and approaches to achieve this, including:

- verbal communication (including speech and vocalisations)
- non-verbal communication strategies (including body language, signs, symbols, pictures, photographs and objects).

Positive behaviour support

Provides a way of working with people who present challenging behaviour using preventative and constructive approaches, which involves:

- careful assessment of the function of the challenging behaviour
- changing the situation so that setting and triggering events are removed
- teaching new skills that replace challenging behaviour
- minimising natural rewards for challenging behaviour
- an emphasis on improving overall lifestyle quality.

Person-centred planning

A process of working with people to help them identify and achieve the things they want, drawing not only on services they can get but also on the resources of their families, friends and of their community. It is based on the values of inclusion and provides tools for:

- discovering what is important to the person (in their day-to-day life or the future) and what support they require
- creating action plans so that the person has more of what is important to them in their life, with the support that they require
- continuing to reflect and act on the actions in the plan.

Person-centred thinking

Is the development of the five basic skills and seven tools used in essential lifestyle planning to help staff to think and plan in person-centred ways. Person-centred thinking skills include:

- separating what is 'important to' from what is 'important for' and finding a balance between them

Person-centred active support: A handbook   © Pavilion Publishing (Brighton) Ltd 2010

- defining the roles and responsibilities of those who are paid to support
- getting a good match between those who are paid to provide, and those who use services
- learning, using and recording how people communicate
- supporting 'mindful' learning.

While their origins may differ considerably, it is clear that these approaches have been developed by professionals from a range of disciplines who are fully committed to achieving real change and empowering people with learning disabilities. Few professionals would argue that these approaches are incompatible, but it can be difficult for support workers to see how they fit together.

Managers and staff frequently receive mixed messages about the relevance of particular approaches and implementation priorities from the organisation they work for and from external professionals.

Staff observation

When I became manager here in 2003, there was a real focus on implementing active support. We had a clear implementation plan and were working hard to make each day more predictable for the people who live here. At that time, we were very focused on supporting people to participate, for the first time, in the household activities each day.

Not long after, the area manager announced at the area management meeting that we needed to focus on developing person-centred plans. Getting all the staff trained and producing the person-centred plans in the required format and timescale meant that the person-centred support implementation was abandoned.

Jackie, service manager, London

Individuals, particularly those who have been working in social care for some time, have a tendency towards a polarisation which works against real understanding of an integrated approach. Many have developed a narrow focus on particular approaches to support which is strongly influenced by their training and background. Where these people are practice leaders, there is a danger that they will prioritise and reinforce their preferred approach. For this reason, a considerable number of people we support and staff experience major shifts in focus and expectations when there are personnel changes in practice leadership positions.

It is important for organisations, practice leaders and staff to recognise that there is no one approach or set of tools that will lead to the changes people want and need from services and staff.

The development of person-centred approaches requires staff to utilise a combination of approaches that are matched to the person's needs and preferences. Integrating approaches provides a more comprehensive means of improving the quality of support people receive than one particular approach alone.

Observation

During the feedback at the end of some person-centred thinking training I had been facilitating, one of the participants asked if the tools she had been learning about replaced the active support tools they had in the service.

One of the other participants on her table answered her question by saying, 'The person-centred tools don't replace active support but will help us to implement it better. It's like a toolkit. We already have lots of active support tools like shift plans and graded levels of assistance in our toolkit. After these two days, we'll have some new tools which we can pick out to learn more about people.'

Bev, practice development co-ordinator, United Response

The Way We Work Framework (see **figure 1**) was developed by United Response to help staff see how the different approaches work together to improve the lives of the people being supported by dividing the work staff do into four areas.

Values: The main aim is to encourage individuals to plan for and take control of their lives and spell out what this would mean in practice.

Listening: Identifying different ways in which the service and staff can hear what people are saying.

Organising: Recognising that resources have to be organised to make real changes in a person's life.

Reviewing: Emphasises that it isn't just one process, but a family of activities that help the service learn how to do its job better.

Figure 1: United Response, The Way We Work Framework

The framework is used in staff training and team meetings to promote an integrated approach. The format is also used to assess what is working and not working in each section and to help staff and teams develop individual and service plans.

Person-centred planning, thinking and action

Person-centred planning, person-centred thinking and person-centred action are not alternatives. They are complementary parts of the same process.

Person-centred planning, a process designed to assist a person to make plans for their future, was adopted as government policy in the United Kingdom through the Valuing People white paper in 2001, and is accepted as good practice in many countries throughout the world. Person-centred thinking is a set of value-based skills that help staff to think and plan in person-centred ways.

In order to change the lives of people with learning disabilities, staff need to be able to turn person-centred thinking and planning into person-centred action (see **figure 2**).

For people with significant disabilities, person-centred action will always involve providing direct practical support to the individual to help them make the most use of the opportunities available in their life. For the majority this help will include person-centred active support, positive behaviour support and a variety of communication strategies.

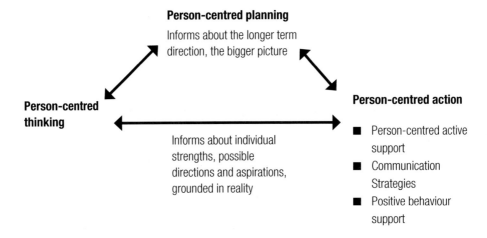

Person-centred planning
Informs about the longer term direction, the bigger picture

Person-centred thinking

Informs about individual strengths, possible directions and aspirations, grounded in reality

Person-centred action

- Person-centred active support
- Communication Strategies
- Positive behaviour support

Figure 2: Cycle of person-centred thinking, planning and action

Person-centred planning provides a sense of direction, a perspective on the bigger picture and motivation; person-centred thinking provides better knowledge and understanding which can then be translated into person-centred action through person-centred active support, communication strategies and positive behaviour support.

Supporting people to engage in meaningful activities and relationships provides valuable information about the individual strengths, preferences and needs, and helps to identify possible directions and aspirations which are grounded in reality, which should be used to inform person-centred thinking and person-centred planning.

> *'Only when the 'circle of support' helping to organise a person-centred plan knows the person well enough, can they help make realistic goals and achieve progress. It is much easier to know the person if it is based on a real relationship that involves practical help to engage in meaningful activity and relationships. You learn much more by supporting people to do things than by sitting with them while they do nothing.'*
>
> Mansell *et al*, 2005

Person-centred active support at home

While most other adults with learning disabilities live in some kind of communal housing, an increasing number of people now have supported living arrangements which are more individual and give them more say about how they live.

The implementation of person-centred active support and its positive impact on the quality of people's lives in residential services is well documented, but we frequently meet with managers and staff who are struggling to see how person-centred support fits in with the principles of supported living.

Peter Kinsella (1993) lists the five principles of supported living as the following.

1. **Separating housing and support**

   The agency that provides or co-ordinates support is not the landlord, nor does it have any organisational connection to the property owner.

2. **Focusing on one person at a time**

   A process of person-centred planning is used to find out what each individual person wants, and then to plan individually and assist them to secure the accommodation and supports that are right for them.

3. **Full user choice and control**

   Individuals choose where they live, who they live with (if anyone), who supports them and how. Individuals hold their own tenancy or mortgage and are in control of their own money and household.

4. **Rejecting no one**

   There is an implicit assumption that everyone can live in the community. The fact that someone has complex needs does not mean they should be denied the opportunity to choose their own lifestyle. Attention is given to environmental adaptations and personally designed supports.

5. **Focusing on relationships, making use of informal supports and community resources**

   The starting point is to build on a person's existing relationships and connections. Paid help is only used when natural and informal support is not available and can be used to develop a person's social network alongside other activities.

The principle of 'rejecting no one' suggests that environment and support provided is matched to each individual's needs and preferences. But as with all broad social policy goals, the application of these abstract concepts to people with severe and profound learning disabilities can be difficult.

For example, the principle of 'full user choice and control' can be very confusing for staff supporting people with severe and profound learning disabilities in practice, when understanding effective support for choice and control requires:

- identifying the person's preferences by observing and recording verbal and non-verbal responses in a variety of situations
- broadening people's experiences by providing a range of opportunities for engagement and interaction

- shaping up the individual's choice and control over time by introducing choice gradually without overwhelming or confusing
- making a best guess about what the person would choose in particular situations or circumstances.

When considering choice and control on a daily basis, staff supporting people with complex needs also need to make a wide range of 'best guesses' and be aware of the dangers associated with interpreting resistance or challenging behaviour as a choice not to participate (see Chapters 12 and 13).

Observation

Throughout an evaluation visit to a service in York, which had recently deregistered, I noted that people's involvement in activities had decreased considerably. On my previous evaluation visit, I had seen people participating in meal preparation on a 'little and often' basis but on this occasion the people being supported sat in the lounge or in their bedrooms throughout the meal preparation without participating in activities and very little interaction with staff.

During my feedback to the team members on duty, I asked them about this and they explained that as the service had now become 'supported living', it was people's choice not to do these things. They explained that where previously they would have told people it was time to prepare the dinner and then brought materials to them and provided physical support for them to be involved, they now asked people if they wanted to do it and if they did not respond, they took this as a no and did if for people instead.

Bev, practice development advisor, United Response

Without clarification of how the broad principles of supported living work in practice, there is a danger that because these considerations appear to conflict with person-centred active support, the quality of the support provided in these services will reduce and the rich opportunities for engagement in meaningful activities and relationships within these environment will not be fully utilised.

Person-centred active support at work

The goal of an 'ordinary working life' has not become a reality for many people we support, particularly those with profound and multiple learning disabilities. While a small percentage of people are in full or part-time employment, the majority spend their days in sheltered workshops, in day programmes, pursuing leisure activities or at home retired or effectively unemployed. Many do not experience the separation of home, work and recreation, originally envisaged in the 'ordinary life' philosophy (King's Fund Centre, 1980).

While people may still leave the house to go to a day centre or work placement, the closure of local authority day services has often resulted in reduced opportunities to leave the house. Furthermore, the development of individualised day support packages means it is not usual for day service staff to come to a person's home or for residential staff to be responsible for supporting people during their 'working day'.

Valuing Employment Now (DH, 2009) sets out an ambitious goal to increase radically the number of people with learning disabilities in employment by 2025. Achieving this would mean to have 48% of people with moderate and severe learning disabilities having real jobs and it would require the employment of an additional 45,000 people with learning disabilities.

Local authorities are in the process of developing their day services. This process commonly includes the closure of large day centres and the development of specialist facilities for people with profound and multiple learning disabilities, community bases and a range of community activity projects (including leisure, arts, education and work training). Learning disability partnership boards are being encouraged to review these plans to ensure that proposals outlined in Valuing Employment Now are incorporated, and that any employment projects that do not themselves provide paid jobs offer a clear short-term pathway to real work.

Services supporting working-age adults with learning disabilities are being encouraged to embed employment into the service and the person-centred support planning, and to effectively utilise a variety of sources to fund supported employment. Yet, where services have acquired additional funding to replace local authority day service provision for individuals or groups, the programmes which are developed usually focus on community presence and leisure activities. In our experience, it can be hard to see the difference between these day activity programmes and residential support.

Reversing this trend will require services to focus on planning and developing employment or work experience opportunities. Having clear aims and objectives in this area can help teams to 'stretch' their thinking and produce creative and practical employment opportunities.

Valuing Employment Now describes supported employment as:

> '... a way for people with learning disabilities to access and retain open employment, with support. Within this, a customised approach starts from the premise that severely disabled people may not be able to compete in the labour market, even with reasonable adjustments. A job coach therefore negotiates a bespoke (customised) job that matches the individual's interests and talents, before supporting the person in work as with supported employment.'
>
> Department of Health, 2009

Effective support for people with profound and multiple learning disabilities with additional impairments will involve providing direct practical support to the individual to help them make the most use of the opportunities available in their life. Applying person-centred active support is an effective way to organise and structure this support, and it ensures people are as actively involved in all the activities and relationships available in the workplace.

Person-centred active support in the community

Most people with learning disabilities have small and restricted social networks, which are characterised by interaction with other people with learning disabilities, staff and immediate family members. Their contact with non-disabled members of the public is likely to be routine, impersonal and brief, although they may have some casual acquaintances. Sustained meaningful relationships with non-disabled people, characterised by familiarity and friendship are typically lacking.

Services are often good at supporting people to be present in their community (e.g. using the local shops and going to the local pub) but levels of meaningful engagement in community activities and relationships are often low.

Increasing the frequency and variety of community-based activities, and the quality and extent of social relationships are important goals in services for people with learning disabilities. Staff are tasked with supporting people to access community facilities, activities and social networks so that they depend less on services and enjoy instead a network of friends and associates in their neighbourhoods. There are three main stages to this work.

Stage one: Getting to know the individual

Finding out what people want to do and what they have to offer, by identifying the person's character, skills, gifts and interests.

Stage two: Getting to know the local community

Finding out what community activity is happening in the local area: Firstly, making a map of the organisation and focal points in the area. Secondly, asking people to share their knowledge of the area to find out about the less visible aspects of community life, the informal gatherings, shared interest groups and so on. This information gathering stage also identifies people who are key contacts to get to know in the area.

Stage three: Connecting people to their local community

With the information gathered about community life and the individual, the next stage is to make a connection. The idea of a connection is not to simply find more activity for someone to be involved in, but to find meaningful roles for people. It should be an opportunity not only to meet people willing to support the individual, but for the individual to support other people too. Staff's role at this stage is to support the person to make the connection, ensuring the person is supported in the ways they need, but to be in the background as much as possible so that people don't have to go through the staff to interact with the person.

When supporting people to make community connections, they are working to enable the person being supported to actively engage in the activities and interactions going on around them and success often depends on knowledge of and consistent support around, details, e.g. learning and respecting the unspoken rules of the group, remembering and supporting the person to complete what they said they would do, being on time, supporting people to offer to buy a round instead of always having it bought for them, etc.

Where detailed planning and skilled support is required to make these connections work, particularly for people with profound and severe learning disabilities and complex needs, the application of person-centred active support is invaluable and increases the changes of success considerably.

Staff observation

During Mark's annual review 12 months ago, we looked at ways we could develop friendships with people in the community. We identified the places we support him to go to and discussed how these could be developed further.

As Mark likes going to the local pub on Tuesdays to see the pool team play, we thought this was a good place to start. We reviewed what was working and not working and found that each staff member supported Mark in a different way. Some people sat with Mark on a separate table and went to the bar for him, others supported Mark to sit at the same table as the pool team and remained in the background, going over to support him at the bar when needed.

> We developed a clear support plan to ensure that we all knew about the pool team and the people Mark had got to know and to make sure we consistently supported Mark to sit at the table with them. We also developed a recording system to ensure that information about what happened each time was passed on to the person supporting him the next week.
>
> I went with Mark last week and when we arrived, one of his friends on the team told me I could go back to the house and pick him up later. 'No point you hanging around here,' he said, 'we'll help him to the bar if he needs a drink'.
>
> Julia, team member, Suffolk

Summary

The development of person-centred approaches requires staff to utilise a combination of approaches that are matched to the individual's needs and preferences. Real change in people's lives will only be achieved when person-centred thinking and planning result in person-centred action.

Person-centred active support is effective in developing meaningful participation in activities and relationships at home, at work and in the community, and it is relevant and useful in a wide range of service models.

Chapter 12

Person-centred active support and people with complex needs

'Every activity has some easier components that people with severe or profound disabilities can get involved in.... Everyone can make some contribution, even if not for long and not very much.'

Mansell *et al*, 2005

Research and anecdotal information consistently shows a direct relationship between the degree of disability and the quality of life experience. This means that person-centred active support is even more important for the people we support who have complex needs such as physical disabilities and autism.

Supporting people with profound and multiple learning disabilities

Many people with profound and multiple learning disabilities spend long periods of time with nothing to do because it is not immediately obvious either that they want to be engaged, or how to enable them to be so.

In the majority of services for people with profound and multiple learning disabilities, those being supported are well cared for, live in clean and comfortable surroundings in the community, have their physical needs met and are regarded positively by staff. However, engagement levels are low (and in many cases non-existent). Discussions with staff indicate that engagement has a low priority for the following reasons:

■ staff believe that people will never have the skills or physical ability to do even parts of the activities independently

- staff have misgivings about the relevance of engagement for the people they are supporting (e.g. they view engagement as meaningful only if the activity itself is meaningful to the person)
- staff are already busy doing things that are part of daily life for people
- staff are focused on ensuring the medical and physical needs of people are met
- attempts to support people to be engaged in activities have been unsuccessful in the past.

Identifying opportunities

Staff can find it difficult to see how person-centred active support 'works' when they are supporting people with profound and multiple learning disabilities. This is often related to a misunderstanding that people can only engage in meaningful activities and relationships, if they can be completely independent in carrying them out. It is important that staff in these services understand that engagement in daily activities and relationships provide opportunities for interaction and the development of predictability, personalised routines and a meaningful environment as well as a platform for other engagement within the wider world.

Staff need to be supported to think about activities differently using the components of person-centred active support discussed in Chapter 3. This support needs to include specific examples of the application of these components and to address misconceptions about person-centred active support for people with profound and multiple learning disabilities.

Instead of thinking about increasing independence within an activity or interaction, it is more meaningful when working with people with profound and multiple learning disabilities to focus on developing the person's 'relationship' to activities. Marvin (1998) suggests the framework outlined below in **table 1** for supporting and evaluating involvement in activities.

Table 1: Encounter to attainment framework	
Encounter	Being present during the experience
Awareness	Noticing that something is going on
Responsive	Showing surprise, dissatisfaction, enjoyment
Engagement	Directed attention, focused looking and listening, showing interest, recognition or recall
Participation	Sharing, turn taking, anticipation, supported involvement

Person-centred active support: A handbook © Pavilion Publishing (Brighton) Ltd 2010

Table 1: Encounter to attainment framework	
Involvement	Active participation, reaching out, joining in, doing, commenting
Attainment	Gaining, consolidating, practising skill, knowledge, concept and understanding

By considering where in this framework the person is in relation to the activity (see **table 2**) staff can plan how they present the activity to help progression.

Table 2: Encounter to attainment plan			
Current level of involvement		✓	**Details of current involvement:**
Level 1	Encounter	✓	Peter is in the kitchen by the bench, while the team member prepares the vegetables for dinner.
Level 2	Awareness		
Level 3	Responsive		**Steps it will take for this person to increase involvement:**
Level 4	Engagement		Team members will move the chopping board and vegetables onto Peter's wheelchair tray, where they will chop the vegetables. This will bring things within his line of vision so he is more likely to notice.
Level 5	Participation		
Level 6	Involvement		
Level 7	Attainment		

Observation

I supported a team who worked with five people with profound and multiple learning disabilities and in particular, substantial physical disabilities. They struggled to identify how they could support people in a black and white way, which is, either the person can do it or they can't do it.

It created a block to any progress. When we talked about a continuum of engagement, it suddenly released a lot of potential. They'd got stuck into believing that if a person could be actively involved in an activity, their willingness to do so would be obvious and their engagement would be tangible and clear. To think about it as a path they can follow made a big difference to how they viewed people being present during, aware of and responding to activity. They began to see it as a potential opportunity rather than a failure.

John, practice development advisor, United Response

Effective physical support

People with profound and multiple learning disabilities usually need effective physical support to facilitate participation and learning, without it these people can remain immobile and isolated.

Person-centred active support promotes the importance of engagement and participation and encourages the use of graded levels of assistance (outlined in Chapter 3) to help staff identify the types and levels of assistance they can use to achieve this. Enabling people with profound and multiple learning disabilities to participate often requires staff to develop their understanding and skills in using physical assistance cues with greater subtlety.

Understanding rejection

Rejection of involvement in activities is commonly experienced by staff providing support to people with profound and multiple learning disabilities. There are two ways to look at this:

1. the rejection is the person saying they don't like or want to be involved in this activity; or
2. rejection is the expected reaction of people who:
    a. have limited experience of enjoyable activity
    b. have difficulties understanding what activities might be about
    c. are supported by people who will do the same thing differently
    d. may not understand the time sequences
    e. are used to doing nothing
    f. have limited (or no) experience of controlling what happens
    g. experience things 'coming out of the blue' at them.

It is important that the team supporting people with profound and multiple learning disabilities appreciate the virtue and benefits of the second approach.

The model shown in **figure 1** suggests that rejection is merely the first and expected stage in a sequence of responses to opportunity and that by continuing to offer opportunities despite the initial rejection (and doing so with care, sensitivity and predictability) people can be supported to move through other stages (accepts passively, enjoys, signals for more, initiates).

Observation

When talking about why people reject opportunities, I am frequently struck by the expectations we have of people we support. I have to remind myself of how reluctant I am to try something new, how I try and work out what might happen before I go somewhere unfamiliar, how often I say no to something I might enjoy just because I'm unsure about it. Despite agreeing that this is not unusual, colleagues are frequently reluctant to allow its relevance for people who might reasonably be supposed to be even more uncertain about unfamiliar opportunities than me.

John, practice development advisor, United Response

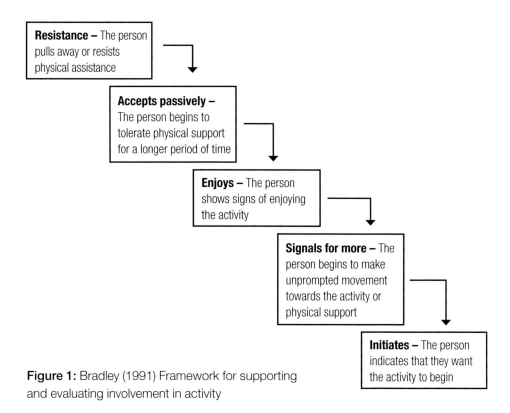

Resistance – The person pulls away or resists physical assistance

Accepts passively – The person begins to tolerate physical support for a longer period of time

Enjoys – The person shows signs of enjoying the activity

Signals for more – The person begins to make unprompted movement towards the activity or physical support

Initiates – The person indicates that they want the activity to begin

Figure 1: Bradley (1991) Framework for supporting and evaluating involvement in activity

The crucial concept that staff need to grasp is that a rejection is not necessarily a choice of 'no' as opposed to a 'yes', but might very well be a 'no, not yet' – a necessary stage on the way to positive choice making and meaningful engagement.

To do this staff may need to:

1. know and understand the pathology of the person's physical condition and how it may interact with the physical support they provide
2. work with the physiotherapist to identify appropriate positioning and support and to understand and anticipate the person's physical responses to support

3. recognise the different types of resistance they may encounter and identify the appropriate response.

Refusal = resistance which tells us the person does not want to participate in this activity at this time.

Involuntary resistance = resistance as a result of high tone or spasticity.

Involuntary passivity = resistance as a result of low tone.

Resistance = which is due to uncertainty, fear or lack of understanding.

Responding correctly to the different types of resistance, which are not absolute refusal, enables staff to support people to move through other stages in the sequence as shown in **figure 2**.

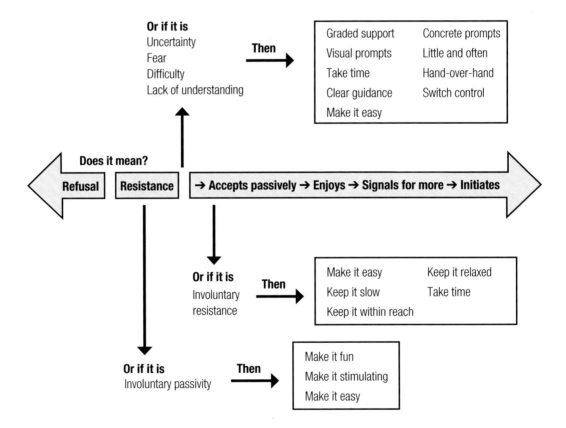

Figure 2: Effective physical support: responding to resistance

Whenever staff are providing physical support to people with profound and multiple learning disabilities, it is vital that they continually listen to verbal and non-verbal responses from the individual and utilise this information to develop and improve the physical support they provide.

Recognising and celebrating achievements

As discussed in Chapter 8, recognising and celebrating achievement plays an important role in staff's motivation to implement person-centred active support and to continue to involve people in activities. Because the outcomes for people with profound and multiple learning disabilities are often more difficult to see (e.g. the move from resistance to tolerance) recording progress may look different and require more forethought.

The form in **figure 3** combines information from the 'Improving your support skills' worksheet (seen in Chapter 3) with the Marvin (1998) framework to enable staff to record the individual's participation and current responses to physical assistance. It is a sampling tool (as discussed in Chapter 10) which is completed at regular intervals (normally between one and three months) to record if change has occurred.

Periodic review of participation and responses to physical assistance									
Name of person being supported: Date:									
Breakdown of the activity	On own	With help	Staff do	Support notes	Resistant	Accepts passively	Enjoys	Signals for more	Initiates

Figure 3: Periodic review of participation and responses to physical assistance

Practice leadership

As discussed in detail in Chapter 7, effective practice leadership is necessary for the successful implementation of person-centred active support. Practice leaders in services for people with profound and multiple learning disabilities also need to:

- manage the balance between responding to people's health needs and the need to support people effectively to participate in a range of activities and relationships
- ensure staff have the knowledge, skills and confidence to consistently provide effective physical support
- model good practice and provide coaching in the use of effective physical support and working with resistance
- effectively review progress to identify and celebrate small changes in involvement.

Person-centred active support and people with autism spectrum disorders

'Autism is a lifelong developmental disability. It is part of the autism spectrum and is sometimes referred to as an autism spectrum disorder, or an ASD. The word "spectrum" is used because, while all people with autism share three main areas of difficulty, their condition will affect them in very different ways. Some are able to live relatively "everyday" lives; others will require a lifetime of specialist support.

'The three main areas of difficulty which all people with autism share are sometimes known as the "triad of impairments". They are:

- difficulty with social communication
- difficulty with social interaction
- difficulty with social imagination.'

The National Autistic Society, 2010

The SPELL framework (Mills, 2008) has been developed to form the basis of training and the provision of services for people with autism, and uses cognitive learning theory to instil five key pillars of good practice:
- Structure
- Positive approaches and expectations
- Empathy
- Low arousal
- Links

This framework is described in Beadle-Brown *et al* (2009) as recognising the individuality of all people with autism. It highlights the importance of planning for and supporting people on that basis. SPELL is a foundation on which to build other person-centred approaches and interventions. Person-centred active support involves providing enough help to enable people to participate successfully in meaningful activities and relationships so that people gain more control over their lives, gain more independence and become more included as a valued member of their community, irrespective of the degree of intellectual disability or the presence of extra problems. For this reason, person-centred active support is well-matched to the five key pillars of good practice within the SPELL framework.

To demonstrate this, we will provide a more detailed explanation of each pillar and identify where this links to specific person-centred active support principles and tools discussed elsewhere in this book.

Structure

The value of structure in the lives of people with autism is well evidenced. It involves the use of supports such as visual timetables, environmental management and other non-verbal communication aids to make the world more comprehensible and predictable and thus reduce anxiety.

Providing structure helps people to organise and make sense of what can be a very confusing world. Predictable events and activities lead to a reduction of anxiety.

Structure is not the same as rigid routine. It does not mean that the person has to do the same thing every day, or that they cannot try new things, or that everyone has to do the same thing. It can, in fact, be important to build change into people's routines, in a careful and managed way, in order to encourage flexibility. Choice-making opportunities are important but need to be offered in a way that is accessible to each individual – closed choices with two or three alternatives (such as, 'would you like to peel the potatoes or the carrots?') are much more successful than open-ended choices with no visual cues (such as, 'what would you like to do today?').

Links to person-centred active support – essentials of person-centred active support (Chapter 3), increasing predictability (Chapter 4) increasing consistency (Chapter 5).

Positive approaches and expectations

Positive attitudes and appropriate expectations help to enhance people's confidence and self-esteem. Providing activities and interactions helps people to recognise and develop their strengths and skills, but not such high expectations that people are filled with anxiety and lack of confidence. This involves engaging with people in meaningful activities and relationships by supporting them to do things successfully and safely, so they can make choices, learn and grow in independence.

Positive approaches are also about how people with autism are portrayed to others including, the language and imagery staff use, the activities people are offered and the way people are supported to become valued members of their community.

Links to person-centred active support – principles of engagement and participation (Chapter 1), essentials of person-centred active support (Chapter 3), increasing consistency (Chapter 5).

Empathy

Empathy is about respecting people's differences and working to understand how they experience the world around them or in a given situation. It is about understanding how people think, learn and communicate and finding ways to help them function as well as possible in what may seem to them an alien world.

Empathy is not about acknowledging the difficulties the individual faces and then allowing them to avoid any difficult situation, but supporting them through these difficulties using rehearsal of potentially difficult scenarios, positive approaches, expectations and structure.

Links to person-centred active support – the importance of engagement and participation (Chapter 1) little and often, choice and control (Chapter 3) increasing predictability (Chapter 4) increasing consistency (Chapter 5).

Low arousal

This element of the SPELL framework applies to both the environment and interactions with a person and is important to improve focus and concentration, but it is also key in reducing anxiety and managing 'challenging behaviour'. It recognises that the sensory profile of individuals with autism often differs markedly from that of the general population in that they may be either over- or under-sensitive across the full range of sensory domains.

Low arousal involves providing person-centred environments that are uncluttered and that offer opportunities for the person to relax and relieve tension. It also involves interactions that are calm, focused and planned and which adopt a non-confrontational style. Giving people the opportunity to experience new and potentially anxiety-provoking events or activities in very small chunks, with control over the course of the activity, will help them to be able to engage in activities and interactions in the future.

Links to person-centred active support – essentials of person-centred active support (Chapter 3), increasing predictability (Chapter 4) increasing consistency (Chapter 5).

Links

This element is focused primarily on supporting integration in mainstream society through consistency and continuity of approach. Open links and communication between people

Person-centred active support: A handbook   © Pavilion Publishing (Brighton) Ltd 2010

(e.g. parents and support staff) will provide a holistic approach and reduce the possibility of unhelpful misunderstanding, or confusion, or the adoption of fragmented, piecemeal approaches.

Links to person-centred active support – the importance of engagement and participation (Chapter 1) increasing consistency (Chapter 5) promoting team work (Chapter 6) monitoring and reviewing (Chapter 10) links to other approaches (Chapter 11).

All staff supporting people with autism must have a good understanding of autism and of good practice. When this is combined with effective implementation of person-centred active support, then effective person-centred support for people with autism spectrum disorders can result. If we look at the four essential components of person-centred active support discussed in Chapter 3, there are some additional considerations that will improve this fit.

Every moment has potential

Staff look for opportunities to support people to participate in meaningful activities and interactions throughout the day.

Generally, this involves encouraging staff to involve the people they are supporting in whatever activity needs to be done or is available then and there. When thinking about this in relation to people with autism, it can be more useful to think in terms of their sensory preferences. There will be some types of sensory stimulation that an individual either loves or hates and this will have a significant impact on whether they get involved in the activity or not.

Sensory preferences can also affect which parts of activities the person participates in and for how long, e.g. some people don't like using their hands because they are so sensitive, which means they may only touch things briefly. Staff need to understand such preferences and give the person as much control over the course of the activity as possible.

Little and often

Making and taking time to involve people in activities and interactions 'little and often', in order to build up experience of success and increase motivation.

Often staff are the biggest source of sensory stimulation, and therefore the most anxiety-provoking thing in the environment, a situation which is made worse when they are rushing around trying to do activities quickly and efficiently.

Many of the people we support are mono-attentive, which means they can only process one type of sensory input at a time. If staff are 'multi-tasking', these people will be unable to follow staff's movements, process what they are doing and consequently what they themselves should be doing. All of which makes it more important that staff make and take time to focus on involving people.

Many people with autism have a history of failure in participating in activities and interactions and need to build up experience of success. People with autism have a tendency to remember bad experiences and to make associations with details that were involved (e.g. if they had a bad experience of being involved in hoovering, the next time they see the hoover they may become agitated and staff may not know why). New and potentially anxiety-provoking activities need to be introduced in small doses. Because people can easily experience sensory overload, it may be important to allow people to take breaks and engage in repetitive behaviours, as a coping technique, during activities.

Graded assistance to ensure success

Providing the right kind and level of assistance to ensure the person experiences success.

Each of the types and levels of assistance described in Chapter 3 is an additional sensory input for the person with autism to process. It is important that staff give the person sufficient time to process and respond to each type of sensory input, though clearly there needs to be a balance between this and making them wait too long.

For many people with autism, it can be difficult to recognise objects or identify what they are for. This makes ensuring that the visual information relating to the activity and interaction is clear, and giving the person feedback that they have got it right is particularly important.

Mono-attention can also have an impact on the use of physical contact during activities e.g. touching someone during an activity can result in the person only processing this tactile information, distracting them from processing visual or audio information. The use of physical assistance needs to be avoided or carefully planned in many cases.

Maximising choice and control

Maximising the opportunities for the person to have choice and control as activities unfold.

For people with autism, shaping up their choice and control means respecting their preferences (including their sensory preferences). Where these are not clear, staff teams will need to observe and record people's behaviour in a variety of situations to find out what they are. During activities and interaction, staff need to give the person an easy way to express their choice, without overloading them, and then respect those choices.

Broadening experiences for people with autism requires staff to provide a range of opportunities for engagement and interaction. The best way to start is with things that provide them with the sensory stimulation they like. To do this effectively, staff need to understand what these are and preferably experience these as best as they can by trying the activities the person does to stimulate themselves and identify how it feels and what might be nice about it. Doing this will enable staff to think about what other activities might feel like this and plan their introduction of a new activity.

Intensive interaction

Many people with complex needs present particular challenges because the most fundamental components of communication seem to be absent. Staff will often describe them as 'being difficult to reach'. The expectation that we will be able to support such people immediately into engagement in meaningful activity is understandably viewed with concern, and sometimes with scepticism.

Staff observation

I'd been on some active support training and thought about how best to support Tracy, but I just couldn't get over my doubts about her being involved in anything practical. She won't hold anything, she can't move much, she barely looks at anything you do near her, and although we talk to her, I can't say that we've ever known her to respond.

It sounds harsh but I just didn't think she would do anything with us at all. I certainly couldn't imagine her doing anything significant around the house or out in the community.

Penny, service manager, London

Our experience is that we must acknowledge this reality but we have promoted the view that if the person's experience and disability has led them to be disconnected from the world, the activities and people that fill it, then this must be because the world appears to them to be insufficiently interesting or understandable. As such, it is our job not just to accept their disconnection from interaction and activity as inevitable and unavoidable, but to take on the task of making the world make sense to the person.

Intensive interaction is an approach that we have found to be particularly successful in bridging the gap between people with severe learning disabilities or autism and their surroundings, where this disconnection is significant. It characteristically enables staff and others to make themselves interesting, recognisable and safe to the person, and promotes the development of communication fundamentals such as attention, turn-taking, responding, initiating and leading.

By using techniques that focus on sounds, patterns and movements that the person already has in their repertoire of behaviours, staff have frequently found that they can gain the attention of the person and then develop interactions, usually by keeping things enjoyable, undemanding and responsive, that ultimately can lead both partners in the interaction into other opportunities.

Staff observation

When we talked about trying intensive interaction with Tracy, I think most of us were not very sure about it. However, we decided to give it a go and each of us spent some time sitting as near to Tracy as she seemed comfortable with.

Using the same arm movements and vocal sounds as she does, we guessed that we needed to sit side on to her because we know from doing person-centred care with her that she's happier like that. We were looking for her to notice that we were doing something that she recognised, because she does it herself. In the first week, it didn't seem to be working and we were concerned that it was a waste of time after all. Then one of my colleagues noticed that when I was in the hall with Tracy doing the same noises as her, Tracy stopped rocking and just did the noises, and it was in between when I did them. So we kept going and gradually we began to get some eye contact and she would definitely be more interested in us.

We're all now just doing the same sort of thing all the time with Tracy so it's like how we talk to her. What we want to do next is to move on to use this as an opportunity to get involved in other things. Because she's with us more, we think we can hand her things, though she may drop them quickly, it'll be a start.

Ingrid, team member, London

For people with profound and multiple learning disabilities, such developments will clearly be slow and staff need to remember the essentials of active support discussed in Chapter 3 (certainly 'every moment has potential', but particularly 'little and often', 'graded assistance' and 'maximising choice and control') as they progress from the foundation blocks of attention and interest provided by intensive interaction.

For some people on the autistic spectrum, the effects of using intensive interaction can be remarkable. We have seen people change radically from being isolated and locked into repetitive and stereotyped behaviours to being enthusiastic communicators with an intense interest in the people who use intensive interaction and a willingness to engage with them, in a range of activities that would have previously seemed impossible.

Successful support for people with autism is often a mixture of meaningful activity and repetitive, self-stimulatory behaviour, where assistance to participate is interspersed with moments of intensive interaction to help maintain connection, interest, engagement and receptiveness.

Observation

I was aware that the staff team supporting Des were developing the use of intensive interaction, in conjunction with their local speech and language therapist. However, I wasn't ready for the phone call I got some weeks later in which the service manager described how positively Des had responded to it.

Not only was he out and about and doing things around the house instead of hiding himself away in his bedroom, but he was (for the first time anybody could remember) actively seeking to interact with people, to the point that staff were beginning to struggle with his demands for communication. It wasn't that they resented it, they were just shocked that this person who they thought of as private and reclusive, was in fact desperate to communicate but had never been given an opportunity that made sense to him before.

John, practice development advisor, United Response

Intensive interaction is extensively described in practical detail in the literature (e.g. see Nind & Hewitt, 2001; Caldwell & Horwood, 2007). Although we have found that specialist support and specific training can be very useful in implementing intensive interaction, it is worth remembering that the fundamentals of the approach are no more complicated than the empathetic acknowledgement of the person's unique circumstances and the sensitive development of rapport.

Summary

There are clear benefits for the development of person-centred active support for people with complex needs. Staff in services supporting people with profound and multiple learning disabilities often need to develop ways to increase people's 'relationships' to activities, as well as develop their skills, knowledge and confidence in providing effective physical support. A clear understanding of rejection is needed if people with profound and multiple learning disabilities are to become actively involved in all the activities and interactions which are available in their home and the wider community.

There is a clear fit between the SPELL framework for supporting people with autism and the principles of person-centred active support, but effective services will only result when staff have a good understanding of autism and good practice and have developed systems and support to take account of the needs and preferences of each individual with autism.

Chapter 13

Person-centred active support and positive behaviour support

'... for many people, their history has taught them that there is no point in trying to join in. People have learned that the support they get isn't right, that what they are asked to do is too difficult and that things don't work out. Often, people may not even understand what it is they are being asked to do. Some people have learned to cut themselves off from any opportunities or relationships and live in relative isolation, defending themselves with challenging behaviour.'

Mansell *et al*, 2005

Challenging behaviour has been defined as 'culturally abnormal behaviour(s) of such an intensity, frequency or duration that the physical safety of the person or others is likely to be placed in serious jeopardy, or behaviour which is likely to seriously limit use of, or result in the person being denied access to, ordinary community facilities' (Emerson, 1995).

Whether behaviour is seen as challenging depends on the capacity and ability of an individual or service to cope with it. Research into challenging behaviour suggests the following.

■ In most cases, the challenging behaviour occurs when a person has little control over their life and tries to exercise some control. They might do this by screaming to attract attention, or by pushing someone away if they do not want to be with them.
■ Challenging behaviour may also occur because the person with a learning disability is distressed at his or her inability to make others understand what he or she needs.

Challenging behaviours are often associated with a range of negative personal and social consequences.

- Damage to health or quality of life – challenging behaviours can impair the health or quality of life of the person, those who care for them and those who live or work in close proximity.
- Abuse – the difficulties involved in caring for people with challenging behaviours and, in particular, the management of episodes of challenging behaviour, may at times lead to inappropriate reactions from carers and staff.
- Inappropriate treatment include the following:
  - the widespread use of anti-psychotic drugs
  - the use of mechanical restraints and protective devices to manage self-injury e.g. splints, seat straps etc.
  - risk of exposure to degrading or abusive psychological treatments.
- Exclusion, deprivation and systematic neglect – people with challenging behaviours are significantly more likely to be excluded from community-based services. Once admitted to institutional settings, they are more likely to spend most of their time in materially deprived surroundings, disengaged from their world and avoided by staff. These issues can also arise when people remain in community-based services, with the home becoming more institutional. Typically the environment becomes barren and activities, engagement and contact collectively dwindle.

Positive behaviour support

Approaches to the management of challenging behaviour have often been simplistic and narrowly focused, often influenced by the background of any professionals involved. In the understanding of challenging behaviour, there can be a tendency towards polarisation which works against real understanding. Although many professionals have in the past viewed behavioural and person-centred approaches as incompatible, more and more professionals see how both approaches are environmental in nature. Both frequently involve changing antecedent or environmental conditions, and may involve providing reinforcement independently of behaviour.

Positive behaviour support (PBS) brings together the values and commitment of person-centred approaches with evidence-based methods and skills of behavioural approaches. Positive behaviour support involves changing situations and events that people experience in order to reduce the likelihood that challenging behaviours will occur and increase social, personal, and professional quality in their lives. It is based on these values:

- people are individuals with gifts and hope
- people are members of families, peer groups and society
- people influence their circumstances in personally meaningful ways
- people have the right to be treated with dignity and understanding
- relationships and contexts impact on the quality of a person's life.

These values recognise that people's lives are usually enhanced when they benefit from a variety of activities each day: an active network of friends, neighbours, relatives and acquaintants, reflecting the personal preference of the individual. Positive behaviour support aims to support people to achieve these things regardless of whether we are able to reduce the behaviour we find challenging.

The positive behaviour support process involves a team of individuals working together collaboratively to gather information and create strategies for preventing challenging behaviour.

In order to effectively support people whose behaviour is challenging, teams need to base their support and interactions on a comprehensive understanding of the relevance of the behaviour for the individual. This needs to take account of both the person's immediate situation and environment, and the broader background of their entire life (their past history, physical state, emotional state, personality, coping and other personal skills). Furthermore, both these personal contexts need to be understood within the wider range of physical, social and occupational situations experienced by the person.

Staff observation

Eric can have sustained episodes of physical aggression that can last from a few minutes up to 14 hours and can be directed towards staff and the people he lives with. But it also includes self-injury, screaming, swearing, throwing and breaking furniture and windows, and taking his clothes off. The team were usually perplexed by Eric's challenging behaviour and would often feel disappointed or frustrated when he behaved in this way. There was a sense of 'here we go again' and 'batten down the hatches'. Staff would feel annoyed with Eric and there were often comments like 'but we were having such a good time', or 'he really seemed to be enjoying what he was doing'.

A local psychologist became involved and as she was keen to learn more about Eric's past, she went through the archived notes about him. The picture she subsequently described was one of family trauma: depression, suicide, institutional admissions and abandonment, personal tragedy, broken relationships, abuse and failure.

When the psychologist shared this information with the team, I felt a penny drop. Whilst it didn't give us any clear answers about Eric and his behaviours, it certainly gave us a better understanding of the man. He has been through so much and so many people had come in and out of his life. I could imagine him sitting in his chair, in the lounge at the service, when suddenly a frightening story would pass in his mind – he would have to explode.

Looking around the room during this session, I saw a couple of staff members wipe away tears – his story was so sad and it felt like it was about another Eric and not the man some of us had supported for years.

Since this session, Eric's behaviour has not changed. However, the staff have a greater resolve than they had before. Feelings of frustration and annoyance have been replaced by greater empathy and understanding. I think that the staff team is now more equipped emotionally to deal with his behaviour because at least we now have some sort of context to put it in.

Louise, service manager, London

By providing practice leaders and teams with the knowledge and assessment tools to identify and analyse patterns that suggest the conditions in which behaviour is most likely and least likely to occur, or which may indicate the function(s) of the challenging behaviours, positive behaviour support enables them to develop a better understanding of when and why certain behaviours are likely.

Information that is gathered from the assessment helps the team to develop intervention plans that are *positive, proactive and functional*. Positive behaviour support plans include a number of interventions that can be implemented across situations and settings. These interventions include proactive strategies for:

- changing the environment so triggering events are removed
- developing new skills that replace challenging behaviours
- eliminating or minimising natural rewards for challenging behaviour
- maximising clear rewards for appropriate behaviour

as well as reactive strategies, which are designed to manage the behaviour at the time it occurs.

Positive behaviour support and person-centred active support

While the primary purpose of person-centred active support is not to reduce challenging behaviours, it provides a range of tools and skills which are an important part of the proactive approaches within positive behaviour support.

Our evaluations tell us that people whose behaviour severely challenges, services often receive less person-centred active support from staff and experience lower levels of assistance and contact from staff. These are not inevitable consequences that are inherent to the phenomena of challenging behaviour, and are not the 'fault' of individual staff members but a result of the way in which service systems support (or fail to support) people with challenging behaviour.

Supporting some people to participate in activity can be difficult, particularly when working with someone with a long history of using challenging behaviour as a means of avoiding activity-related demands. Over time, staff can learn that they can successfully avoid challenging behaviours by not placing demands on the person. In these circumstances, implementing person-centred active support with its focus on increasing assistance and opportunities for engagement, can increase the levels of challenging behaviour experienced by staff, and therefore reduce the likelihood of successful implementation.

In order to avoid this, staff need to be skilled at presenting opportunities and providing support in ways which encourage participation, while also minimising the occurrence and impact of challenging behaviour. The interplay between person-centred active support and positive behaviour support plays a major part in the successful implementation of both approaches.

Essentials of person-centred active support

If we consider the four essential components of person-centred active support discussed in Chapter 3, there are some additional considerations that will benefit from further examination.

Every moment has potential

Staff look for opportunities to support people in meaningful activities throughout the day.

There is clear evidence that challenging behaviour can be correlated with an absence of low levels of social contact and involvement in meaningful activities. Greater access to opportunities to participate in a range of activities and interactions can reduce the need for the person being supported to present challenging behaviour to gain these experiences. When thinking about this in relation to people whose behaviour is challenging, it can be useful to:

■ select preferred activities

■ use activities where the person can see an end product to their actions.

■ mix up hard and easy activities or new and familiar activities

■ link activities to something that the person is already interested in

■ link activities to an existing event in the day.

Little and often

Making and taking time to involve people in activities and interactions 'little and often', in order to build up experience of success and increase motivation.

Many people with challenging behaviour have experienced failure throughout their lives. Building a history of success by filling a person's day with more rewards for many accomplishments that often go unnoticed, rather than staff attention being focused on challenging behaviour, is therefore important for many people. Supporting people to take part successfully and celebrating their successes, no matter how small, can also help individuals to become more open to trying new things and be more positive about themselves.

Recognising and responding to people's current involvement preferences and involving people in parts of activities for short periods of time or on a stop-start basis often means that people can participate successfully in a range of activities and experience success and positive interactions with staff.

Graded assistance to ensure success

Providing the right kind and level of assistance to ensure the person experiences success.

Poorly presented demands, the wrong type of support and the wrong amount of support, can all elicit escape behaviours for many of the people we support. As discussed in Chapter 3, people we support prefer different types of assistance and staff should use an approach that the individual is comfortable with. Avoiding repeating failed assistance, which can signal failure for the person being supported and result in feelings of frustration and anxiety, is particularly important when supporting people whose behaviour staff find challenging. Other approaches to providing assistance include:

■ presenting demands or requests singly with immediate consequences

■ rewarding a person's attempt to participate in the activity or interaction

- using an interaction style that conveys confidence
- using behavioural momentum (i.e. making requests a person is highly likely to agree to before asking them to participate).

Maximising choice and control

'… as activities unfold, there are many opportunities to support the person concerned in deciding what to do next.'

Mansell *et al*, 2005

Staff's interpretation of challenging behaviour as an active choice not to participate in activities and interactions is often closely linked to their anxiety and fear of the behaviour or its consequences. So it is particularly important to be clear about what constitutes choice.

As discussed in Chapter 3, a number of things need to be taken into account when considering people's choices about participation in activities and interactions. When supporting people whose behaviour is challenging, it is important for staff to recognise that responses to demands or requests, which staff find challenging, may have been learned over time as a way of avoiding things the person associates with past failure, poor communication and lack of appropriate support.

Enabling the person being supported to have some control over what they do, how they do it and when they can take a break, will help them to take part successfully without needing to use challenging behaviour to control what is going on.

Increasing predictability

Chapter 4 looked in detail at the importance of predictability in the lives of people with learning disabilities and ways that staff teams can plan to ensure this. Here we would like to outline how this links to challenging behaviour and the implementation Positive behaviour support interventions.

The way the day is organised, the sequence and pace of activities and interaction can have a significant impact on challenging behaviour. If the person has no way to predict what is going to happen in the next few minutes or hours, or if routines and rituals that are important to them are ignored or disturbed, challenging behaviour is more likely to occur. Changing the way we plan and organise routines and activities to be more person-centred and take account of the antecedents and consequences of challenging behaviour can significantly reduce its occurrence for some individuals.

Staff observation

I am part of a team who supports Max, a young man with severe learning disabilities whose behaviour of swearing and throwing objects is severely challenging. As part of my positive behaviour support training, I carried out an assessment of Max's behaviour and found that it was sometimes linked to his frequent requests to go for a walk. While team members always acknowledged Max's requests, he didn't always end up going because they were busy supporting other people in the house at the time.

While this wasn't the only antecedent to his challenging behaviour, it was a clear example of something we could do in order to reduce Max's behaviour and make his days better. I discussed this with my manager and the team, and we developed a daily shift planner which included set times for a walk in the morning (straight after breakfast) and afternoon (just before dinner) for him each day.

Since we implemented the shift planner, Max's throwing and shouting behaviour has reduced dramatically and he seems much less agitated.

Sally, senior support worker, Chesterfield

Increasing consistency

While the need to ensure people are supported in the same way by different staff and person-centred active support tools for achieving this are discussed in Chapter 5, it is helpful to consider how consistency of support and activities can help in the provision of effective support for people who present behaviours that staff find challenging here.

Staff presenting and or carrying out activities differently – the way things are prepared, the sequence which is used, the materials involved and the pace – can leave the person being supported confused about what they are doing. In many cases, inconsistent presentation and organisation of activities also results in an increased need for repeated assistance and the need to correct 'mistakes'. All these factors decrease the likelihood that the person will experience the activity as a motivating and rewarding success.

Observation

During a visit to a supported living service, I observed a member of staff supporting Karl to make himself and the team member a cup of tea. Karl confidently put the kettle on and got the cups from the cupboard. After a verbal prompt from the team member, he put the tea bags in the cups and added the

---

> sugar. He then reached for the milk and began to pour it into one of the cups. The team member responded by saying, 'No Karl, you never put the milk in before the water'. Karl looked confused, but stopped and waited until the team member prompted him to pour the water from the kettle.
>
> Later in the afternoon I noticed Karl making another cup of tea with a different member of staff. This time, after putting the tea bag and sugar in the cup, Karl reached for the kettle. The team member said 'Karl you've forgotten to put the milk in the cups'. In response, Karl tipped the milk carton over on the bench and ran out of the kitchen.
>
> Bev, practice development co-ordinator, United Response

The development of consistent approaches to supporting the person is an important part of proactive planning in positive behaviour support. Integrating these approaches into staff support during activities and interactions is one of the key elements to the successful implementation of Positive behaviour support and person-centred active support, so it is important to include information on situations and triggers to avoid, as well as the best way to respond, if the person shows challenging behaviour in all support information.

Practice leadership

Despite the evidence that Positive behaviour support can be effective in reducing the frequency, duration and intensity of challenging behaviour in community settings, professionals, consultants and managers often find it difficult to ensure the behaviour support plans are implemented successfully.

Staff's emotions also play an important role in determining their responses to challenging behaviour. Research has shown that staff experience a range of negative emotions, such as sadness, anger, fear and anxiety in response to incidents of challenging behaviour. Because challenging behaviours are aversive to them, staff may be avoiding providing opportunities for people to participate in activities and interaction in order to escape or avoid the negative emotion elicited by these behaviours. A lack of knowledge and skills around challenging behaviour and the implementation of positive behaviour support plans may affect their confidence when dealing with challenging behaviour and in turn their emotional reactions to it.

It is essential that practice leaders need to take account of staff beliefs, attitudes and emotional responses to challenging behaviour when implementing both positive behaviour support and person-centred active support. If these issues are not addressed, the implementation of both approaches may prove to be unsuccessful for people who present such behaviours.

The importance of skills and motivation in person-centred active support is discussed in Chapter 8. Where staff are supporting people whose behaviour is challenging, goals from Positive behaviour support plans need to be incorporated in service statements and the measures used to indicate if person-centred goals are being met or not.

Practice leaders need to develop the skills and confidence of individual staff in supporting people to participate in activities by ensuring they have a good understanding of the context, antecedent and consequences of people's challenging behaviour and that they understand and can successfully follow the support information provided. Modelling and coaching (Chapter 9) are also particularly important as staff often need to see that the strategies which have been developed to avoid and manage challenging behaviour are appropriate and successful. Practice leaders should also provide regular feedback to each staff member about their use of both the proactive and reactive strategies.

Monitoring and reviewing processes should incorporate information about changes in the frequency, duration and intensity of challenging behaviour with information about engagement in activities. This is important where staff are supporting people whose behaviour is challenging because it may change the ways in which they celebrate success, e.g. it might mean celebrating the fact that behaviour has increased (because the person is engaging more) but that the team are effective at minimising its impact.

Summary

Positive behaviour support involves changing situations and events that people experience in order to reduce the likelihood that challenging behaviours will occur, and increase social, personal, and professional quality in their lives. The aims of person-centred active support are to provide support and assistance rather than demand and control, and promote high levels of interaction and activities and materials that are readily available, which can modify specific antecedents to the challenging behaviours presented by many of the people we support.

The interplay between person-centred active support and Positive behaviour support plays a major part in the successful implementation of both approaches. Practice leaders will need to take this into account when developing good staff support for the people they serve.

Chapter 14

Evaluation

'… powerful though knowledge about individuals is, managers will sometimes need numbers that demonstrate how well person-centred active support is being provided across the service.'

Mansell *et al*, 2005

Evaluation is the systematic and objective assessment of an activity, project, programme, strategy or policy. As part of the development of person-centred active support, evaluation provides timely assessments of the relevance, efficiency, effectiveness, impact and sustainability of implementation. Effective evaluation processes provide valuable information about – are we doing the right thing? Are we doing it right and are there better ways of achieving the results?

This chapter contains the approaches and experience of evaluation from four organisations working directly with people with learning disabilities who are currently implementing person-centred active support, using the following questions.

- Describe your approach to evaluation of person-centred active support.
- What difficulties have you experienced and what solutions have you found?
- How has the evaluation process changed or developed your work as an organisation?
- Are there any future plans for evaluation?

The Avenues Trust, Sidcup, England

Jayne Kilgallen

Describe your approach to evaluation of person-centred active support

Person-centred active support has been incorporated into Avenues' quality assurance systems at all levels of the organisation.

Following the training, all support staff are observed providing support and are given feedback using a coaching style each month by a senior member of staff. This helps to ensure consistency of support provided, highlight areas for development which can feed into supervision and team meetings, and also provides an opportunity to celebrate good practice and build staff motivation.

This is supported by six-monthly observations of service user engagement and the quality of staff support, which are carried out by service managers. Along with observing on these occasions, service managers also audit the paperwork systems in place along with supervision and team meeting minutes to ensure active support is discussed in all cases, and that the progress of service users and staff is monitored and continues to develop. The service manager feeds progress back to the team highlighting successes and areas for development.

In addition, as for the first six services, Avenues continued to collect detailed baseline data on engagement and the quality of staff support in each service prior to the training. This is followed up a year after the training and every other year thereafter, by the person-centred active support co-ordinator from the quality assurance team to ensure that progress is maintained, and to keep the focus on what we are trying to achieve. So far, we have follow-up data on 26 of our services and this has shown that we have maintained the significant findings achieved in the first six services.

What difficulties have you encountered and what solutions have you found?

One difficulty has been managers seeing it as something they have to do in addition to their job as opposed to being part of their job. Managers have sometimes struggled with managing their responsibility to carry out observations and work has been done to ensure they understand the importance of this part of their job and how they can manage their time and workload effectively to incorporate these. Organisational commitment to active support has been absolutely crucial in maintaining focus. The implementation of active support was a key part of our business plan 2006–2009 and remains a key focus in our current plan. All staff and trustees have had in-depth presentations on what active support is and why Avenues is implementing it. All decisions regarding the implementation are made by a project group consisting of senior managers and involving others from different areas when needed. This has helped us to remain focused on what we are working towards and has been useful in ensuring everyone is clear about their roles.

How has the evaluation process changed and developed your work as an organisation?

There has been a radical shift in the organisation from a focus on processes to a focus on outcomes. It has meant that the organisation now has real information on how people are experiencing services, and areas for development can be highlighted and acted upon quickly. We are also getting better at highlighting where things are going well and through looking into why this is the case, we can tailor our support to services where things are not going so well.

Are there any future plans for evaluation?

This is something that Avenues really want to pursue and we are currently talking to the Tizard Centre about how this might be done as well as the need for external verification and evaluation.

Dimensions, Theale, England

Paul Pargeter

Describe your approach to evaluation of person-centred active support

The aim is for six monthly observations to take place, measuring the amount of person-centred active support and engagement in each service. This will enable us to view development and make decisions about further input from reliable information.
In the future, it will be possible to look at data on active support and people's engagement in services, regions and the organisation as a whole. It will be a way of getting a measure on people's quality of life, or at least a big indicator of it.
Progress will also be monitored through balanced scorecards (the system used by all) and other local monitoring and review mechanisms that will be outlined in roll-out plans, as well as through an active support lead's gathering twice a year. This will be a time to share and celebrate good practice and problem-solve ways to clear barriers. The best practice manager draws up twice yearly reports providing the organisation with progress, learning and updates.

What difficulties have you encountered and what solutions have you found?

At the moment, it is a question of capacity and expertise. Our intentions are to train all person-centred active support regional leads, plus all the regional quality leads in observation. We will then have the expertise and capacity to obtain reliable and useful data that will give us a good measure of active support and engagement. Quality leads already visit and audit people's services, so we hope the capacity to carry out observations will be very achievable.

Keeping up the momentum is vital, so organisational executives make efforts to keep up the conversation and support regions to keep on top of their plans. Some central leadership, direction and support is helpful, and this is provided by the best practice manager (part of our central quality team, led by the director of continuous improvement).

How has the evaluation process changed or developed the way you work as an organisation?

There is a greater awareness of the positive impact person-centred active support can bring, and positive stories have pricked up ears across the country. An example of how person-centred active support works in a region can be found in Appendix 1.

A recent development at Dimensions is the introduction of Reach 2 Audits by people with experience of support. As a measure of the level of importance we place on person-centred active support, they have either praised the existence of or recommended in the introduction of person-centred active support in every service thus far.

Jewish Care, Victoria, Australia

Daniel Leighton

Describe your approach to evaluation of person-centred active support

- Initially we undertook a complete external evaluation – the first Australian evaluation recorded in the scientific literature. The evaluation was completed by the Centre for Developmental Disability Health in Victoria (Koritsas *et al*, 2008).
- We utilised 'tick and flick' sheets to collect data on the amount of support provided to each person during a shift. We continue to use modified forms of this data collection, recognising that it collects data on participation rather than engagement. We are currently working on a web-based collection tool for this.
- We undertook pre- and post-support intensity scale evaluation.
- We measured and compared monthly incident reports.
- We measured and compared monthly reports indicating hours of engagement.
- We aim to be a data driven organisation – so perhaps atypical of disability support providers!

What difficulties have you encountered and what solutions have you found?

- The main difficulty has been sustaining staff interest and motivation.
- Secondly, the difficulty has been having the ability to train new staff in person-centred active support practices during the course of natural staff attrition. There are no 'off the shelf' programmes developed for the individual training of new staff beyond providing backfill to the team leader or senior practitioner to model and coach a person.

How has the evaluation process changed and developed your work as an organisation?

Implementation of person-centred active support has enabled us to further focus staff (and organisational) attention on placing the person at the centre of all activity. It has assisted and made easier additional training on person-centred planning, exposing people (staff and people we support) to new ideas, broken down barriers, etc.

Are there any future plans for evaluation?

There are no formal plans at this stage, however, we continue to report monthly to the board on participation rates and refine our data collection, shaping up desired behaviours and practices so that we increase what we now capture. For example, time spent in the community with and without staff support and counting individual and group activities to drive people to pursue more individualised options. We hope that our trial of the web-based data reporting will make this task much easier and in real time so that we can collect and present large data sets easily.

United Response, London, England

Bob Tindall

Describe your approach to evaluation of person-centred active support

Evaluation in United Response is carried out in partnership with the Tizard Centre at the University of Kent. Data collection is carried out by members of the practice development team and the Tizard Centre analyse the information to provide quantitative data identifying factors that impact on the services being provided.

Evaluations consist of:

- consent, and risk or benefit procedures for the people we support
- a service visit to people's home and observation, providing observational data on engagement in meaningful activity, assistance and contact received, challenging behaviour using momentary time sampling, as well as the active support measure, and a review of systems and structures in support of person-centred approaches

- information questionnaires, providing information on the needs, skills and characteristics of the people we support
- staff questionnaires, providing information on practice leadership, knowledge, staff satisfaction and training information.

Following each observation, verbal and written feedback is provided to area and service managers.

A baseline assessment of 343 people with learning disabilities living in 76 residential and supported living services was carried out in 1999–2000, followed in 2005–2006 by evaluations in 138 services supporting 469 people.

Following the evaluation in 2005–2006, it was decided to change the way we evaluate our learning disability services to provide ongoing local and national information on the quality of support and feedback on a number of key practice areas. Rather than carrying out an evaluation of all learning disability services over an 18-month period as in 2000 and 2005–2006, the evaluation is now being spread over a five-year period, with 20% of services selected to be involved each year.

What difficulties have you encountered and what solutions have you found?

During the baseline assessment, staff were resistant to being observed by an external person. Many complained that the process was intrusive and would not produce accurate information. There were also a number of complaints about the use of 'clinical' assessment tools. It was felt that much of this resistance was because staff were not used to or able to see the value of observation and feedback, but we also recognised that we would need to change some of the tool and reporting procedures to help people feel more comfortable and confident in the evaluation process.

Following the baseline assessment, we developed pre-visit information packs to include accessible information about the evaluation, clear consent and risk benefit procedures and additional information about the person coming to do the evaluation. Following appropriate research, we also adapted and shortened the question in the people we support questionnaires. The format of service evaluation reports was also amended to use the now familiar, The Way We Work Framework, to describe good practice, observations and suggestions and recommendations for improving practice. Finally, we revised our feedback systems to be more accessible to staff and the people we support.

Since 2005, the evaluation measures and questions within the staff and people we support questionnaire have evolved further to elicit additional information, including:

communication, use of person-centred thinking tools, person-centred planning, community presence and contact with families and friends.

The time and resources involved in evaluating all services in the same year had a significant impact on the work carried out by members of the practice development team. Board members were also concerned that things could change significantly in the five year gap between evaluations, which lead to the annual 20% evaluation being introduced in 2008.

How has the evaluation process changed or developed your work as an organisation?

Staff attitudes and responses to the evaluation visits and the resulting feedback have changed dramatically since the baseline assessment. The majority of staff see it as a valuable tool to help them develop the support they provide.

The evaluation process has become integrated into the support services, and is individually and collectively received from the practice development team. It is used to develop service and individual plans and the information provided is also used in area and divisional strategic planning.

Results are now reported to the director team and board of trustees annually and provide a valuable quality indicator, which is used to inform organisational strategy and corporate decisions, regarding training and resource management.

Receiving clear information about the levels of assistance and engagement and implementation of person-centred active support annually ensure it remains high on everyone's agenda.

Are there any future plans for evaluation?

Annual evaluations are planned until 2012, during which time we will continue to work in partnership with colleagues at the Tizard Centre to develop the methods and tools used to match the changing needs of the organisation and the people we support.

Summary

Evaluation provides timely assessments of the relevance, efficiency, effectiveness, impact and sustainability of implementation for each organisation which is helping them to refine their approach to person-centred active support. Because learning from these evaluations is overseen by colleagues at the Tizard Centre, it also contributes to wider learning about the implementation and development of person-centred active support in organisations.

Chapter 15

Learning and lessons for the future

For over 10 years, we have worked with a variety of organisations, services, staff team and people with learning disabilities supporting the implementation of person-centred active support. When the changes resulting from implementation of person-centred active support transform people's lives and how they are seen by staff and others, this work has been immensely rewarding. There have also been times when, despite considerable effort, the implementation of active support has not been successful; this is particularly disappointing when we can visualise the benefits such an approach offers.

Key learning points:

Person-centred active support is important

The implementation of person-centred active support enables people to become active participants in their own lives (rather than observers) and is particularly important for people with profound and multiple learning disabilities. Assistance from staff that is more frequent and more person-centred increases the amount of time the people we support are engaged in a range of activities and interactions.

For many people we support, becoming more actively involved has helped them develop new skills or utilise skills they have not used for some time. It is common to see staff attitudes to the people they are supporting change when the way they work moves from 'doing for' to 'doing with'. Supporting people to successfully participate in a range of activities and interactions stops staff seeing them as passive and gives everyone involved real and shared experiences to focus on and communicate about.

The increased predictability of and consistency in people's lives associated with effective implementation of person-centred active support, is important and reassuring for many people we support. Services are more person-centred when staff plan and monitor activities in consultation with or on behalf of the people they support and communicate what is happening in ways that are meaningful to the individual.

Implementation of person-centred active support and effective practice leadership ensures staff are clear that supporting people to engage in meaningful activities and relationships is their core objective, and that they have the skills and confidence to support people effectively in a range of activities and interactions in a variety of settings.

Person-centred active support can be difficult to implement and maintain

A lack of understanding or commitment is a common feature in services which have failed to implement or maintain person-centred active support. If managers and staff teams cannot see the value of supporting people to participate in the activities and interactions going on everyday, their use of the systems, tools and support techniques which make up person-centred active support can be superficial.

Successful implementation is hindered when person-centred active support is misunderstood or misinterpreted to be about the production of paper plans rather than a 'live' process, which enables continual improvements in the quality of the support provided in practice. Poor implementation also occurs when teams put examples they have seen or heard about into practice without thinking about what it is they are trying to achieve: a 'means' with no sense of an 'end'.

The landscape of learning disability services is continually changing and new approaches and innovations are a common feature. Services are often required to respond to requests, and sometimes demands, to implement new ideas and processes by internal and external forces. The introduction and development of new tools and systems can divert staff time and attention away from engagement and effective frontline support.

One size doesn't fit all

While the principles of person-centred active support are relevant in all service models, its implementation, and the systems and structures which support it, often look different (e.g. shift plans, participation records, support profiles) depending on the people being supported, the skills and knowledge of the team members or the practice leader, and the resources available.

Standardised forms and tools often fail to address the specific needs of the service and need to be adapted to be relevant and efficient. Involving the people we support and the team in the development of plans, systems and tools are an effective way to do this because it promotes increased ownership, commitment and motivation.

Practice leadership is important

The development of person-centred active support requires leaders who understand and are committed to implementing and maintaining person-centred active support and who spend much of their time with staff coaching them to provide good, person-centred support. Where this is not available, teams struggle to successfully implement the essential elements of person-centred active support, develop their skills and confidence and stay motivated. We have also noticed that changes in key practice leadership roles (most notably good practice leaders moving on) are a significant factor in services that fail to maintain person-centred active support over time.

Organisational commitment is important

Successful implementation of person-centred active support requires commitment and allocation of resources and can have considerable organisational implications. It is not a 'quick fix' and often requires services and organisations to be critical of the services it provides.

Organisational messages about participation and engagement are important factors in the implementation of person-centred active support. The development of evaluation measures, which focus on the quality of support individuals receive, not only provides a way for senior managers to monitor implementation and measure the impact of person-centred active support but it also sends a very clear message about its importance to all staff.

Further work with organisations, practice leaders and staff teams will enable us to refine our understanding of the approaches and techniques that support and undermine the implementation and maintenance of person-centred active support, and to develop the relevant resources and information for all staff and services.

The future of active support

If people with learning disabilities are to benefit from the inherent opportunities in their lives in the community, they must have 'the right support'. Whether support is being provided in the home, community or the workplace, it must enable people to exercise independence and choice and be part of their community. The 'enabling relationship' between the person being supported and those providing support is the key to this.

In future, services for disabled people will be more 'personalised'. They will be designed around the individual, funded through individual budgets, controlled by the individual or those nominated to speak for them. As services become more tailored to the individual person, it should become easier to recruit staff that have a good relationship with the person they support, to get to know the person's preferences, and to become skilled at facilitating their engagement in meaningful activity and relationships. It will still be important for members of the team to work in a co-ordinated and consistent way, to have access to good training and support, and to provide evidence of the quality of their support. Person-centred active support will continue to provide a framework for doing this.

However services are organised, real change in the lives of the people we support will only be achieved when person-centred thinking, planning and action work together.

Above all, it needs to be understood that action is the only thing that makes any difference in the lives experienced by those we serve. We have learned that person-centred active support enables staff and services to impact directly and coherently on the activities and relationships enjoyed by people with a learning disability, including people with complex needs and challenging behaviour despite their often deprived and marginalised circumstances. Only with a foundation of engagement, activity and interaction can people be supported to realise their goals and aspirations.

References

Ashman B & Beadle-Brown J (2006) *A Valued Life: Developing person-centred approaches so people can be more included*. London: United Response and Tizard Centre at University of Kent.

Babe Ruth (1940) The Official Babe Ruth Website [online]. Available at: www.baberuth.com/about/quotes.html (accessed April 2010).

Beadle-Brown J, Roberts R & Mills R (2009) Person-centred approaches to supporting children and adults with autism spectrum disorders. *Tizard Learning Disability Review* **14** (3).

Bradley H (1991) *Assessing Communication Together: A systematic approach to assessing and developing early communication skills in children and adults with multisensory impairments*. Cardiff: APLD Publications.

Caldwell P & Horwood J (2007) *From Isolation to Intimacy: Making friends without words*. London: Jessica Kingsley Publishers.

Clement T & Bigby C (2010) *Group Homes for People with Intellectual Disabilities: Encouraging inclusion and participation*. London: Jessica Kingsley Publishers.

Department of Health (2001) *Valuing People: A new strategy for learning disabilities for the 21st century*. London: The Stationery Office.

Department of Health (2009) *Valuing Employment Now: Real jobs for people with learning disabilities*. London: The Stationery Office.

Emerson E (1995) *Challenging Behaviour: Analysis and intervention in people with learning disabilities*. Cambridge: Cambridge University Press.

Felce D, de Kock U, Mansell J & Jenkins J (1984) Assessing mentally handicapped adults. *British Journal of Mental Subnormality* **30** (2) 65–74.

Hersey P & Blanchard KH (1988) *Management of Organizational Behaviour: Utilising human resources*. New Jersey: Prentice Hall.

Ingham G (2007) *Motivate People: Get the best from yourself and others*. London: Dorling Kindersley Limited.

References

Jones E, Perry J, Lowe K, Allen D, Toogood S & Felce D (1996) *Active Support: A handbook for planning daily activities and support arrangements for people with learning disabilities. Booklet 2*. Cardiff: Welsh Centre for Learning Disabilities Applied Research Unit.

Jones E, Perry J, Lowe K, Felce D, Toogood S, Allen D & Pagler J (1997) *Active Support Trainers Manual*. Cardiff: Welsh Centre for Learning Disabilities Applied Research Unit.

King's Fund Centre (1980) *An Ordinary Life: Comprehensive locally-based residential services for mentally handicapped people*. London: King's Fund Centre.

Kinsella P (1993) *Supported Living: A new paradigm*. Manchester: National Development Team.

Koritsas S, Iacono T, Hamiliton D & Leigton D (2008) The effect of active support training on engagement, opportunities for choice, challenging behaviour and support needs. *Journal of Intellectual & Development Disability* **33** (3) 247–256.

Mansell J (1998) Editorial. *Tizard Learning Disability Review* **3** (2).

Mansell J, Beadle-Brown J, Ashman B & Ockenden (2005) *Person-centred Active Support: A multi-media training resource for staff to enable participation, inclusion and choice for people with learning disabilities*. Brighton: Pavilion Publishing.

Mansell J, Felce D, Jenkins J, de Kock U & Toogood A (1982) A Wessex home from home: a staffed house for mentally handicapped adults. *Nursing Times* **79** 51–56.

Mansell J, Felce D, Jenkins J, de Kock U & Toogood A (1987) *Developing staffed housing for people with mental handicaps*. Turnbridge Wells: Costello.

Marvin C (1998) Teaching and learning for children with profound and multiple learning disabilities. In: P Lacey and C Ouvry (Eds) *People with profound and multiple learning disabilities: A collaborative approach to meeting complex needs*. London: David Fulton.

Miles MB & Huberman AM (1994) *Qualitative Data Analysis: An expanded sourcebook* (2nd edition). California: Sage.

Mills R (2008) SPELL [online]. Available at: www.nas.org.uk/nas/jsp/polopoly.jsp?d=1351&a=3362 (accessed April 2010).

National Autistic Society (2010) *Autism: what is it?* [online]. Available at: www.nas.org.uk/nas/jsp/polopoly.jsp?d=2493 (accessed April 2010).

Nind M & Hewitt D (2001) *A Practical Guide to Intensive Interaction*. Kidderminster: British Institute of Learning Disabilities.

Nirje B (1969) The normalization principle and its human management implications. In: RB Kugel & W Wolfensberger (Eds) *Changing Patterns in Residential Services for the Mentally Retarded*. Washington DC: Presidential Committee on Mental Retardation.

O'Brien J (1987) A Guide to Life Style Planning: Using the activities catalogue to integrate services and natural support systems. In: BW Wilcox & GT Bellamy (Eds) *The Activity Catalogue: An alternative curriculum for youth and adults with severe disabilities*. Baltimore: Brookes.

O'Brien J & Tyne A (1981) *The principle of normalisation: A foundation for effective services*. London: Campaign for the Mentally Handicapped.

Osgood T (2003) *Never mind the quality, feel the width! Person-centred Planning Implementation & Developmental Disability Services: A polemic of unease* [online]. Available at: http://www.pardigm-uk.org/pdf/Articles/nevermindthequality.pdf (accessed April 2010).

Scotland Department of Health (2000) *The same as you? A review of services for people with learning disabilities* (No. 0748093788) Edinburgh: The Stationery Office.

Smull MW, Sanderson H, Sweeny C, Skelhorn L, George A, Bourne ML & Steinbruck M (2005) *Essential Lifestyle Planning for Everyone*. Stockport: The Learning Community.

Stancliffe RJ, Jones E, Mansell J & Lowe K (2008) Active Support: a critical review and commentary. *Journal of Intellectual and Developmental Disability* **33** (3) 215–24.

Totsika V, Toogood S & Hastings RP (2008) Active Support: Development, evidence base, and future directions. *International Review of Research in Mental Retardation* **35** 205–249.

United Nations (1975) The Declaration on the Rights of Disabled Persons. New York: United Nations.

Wales National Assembly Learning Disability Advisory Group (2001) *Fulfilling the promises: Report to the National Assembly for Wales*. Cardiff: National Assembly Learning Disability Advisory Group.

Wolfensberger W (1972) *The Principle of Normalisation in Human Services*. Toronto: National Institute on Mental Retardation.

Wolfensberger W (1983) Social Role Valorisation: A proposed new term for the principle of normalisation. *Mental Retardation* **21** 234–239.

Appendix 1

Dimensions: communicating person-centred active support

The people we support require a level of support to help them achieve their goals. Person-centred active support is a tool we can use to get the balance between the support they need and independence right.

Every moment has potential
Think about all the jobs you do during a shift at work and try to include the people we support in all of them.

Use graded assistance to ensure success
Use just the right amount of support to ensure the people we support feel they have achieved something meaningful.

By now the people we support should feel included in their community, are as independent as they can possibly be and are able to identify and communicate their needs and choices.

Little and often
Keep activities short and simple, communicate clearly and think about how you need to prepare for the activity.

Maximising choice and control
Plan ahead as much as possible so that the people we support know what will happen next, but remember it is their agenda.

Appendix 2

The practice hit list

Service and location: _____

Completed by:_____ Date:_____

Use the hit list to review current practice and the support received by the people we support. Write comments for each point outlining what evidence you have seen that tells you this is or is not a problem.

Problem	Comments
Over estimating people's level of verbal understanding	
Actual activity levels are low	

Problem	Comments
Activities and interactions are not appropriate	
Inappropriate perception of time e.g. staff do things in a fast and efficient way rather than taking the time to do things with the people they support. Staff are not conveying the passage of time in a way that makes sense to people, e.g. saying, 'I'll be back in five minutes'	
Lack of consistency	
Bad use of the physical environment e.g. ■ Collision points ■ Things kept in the wrong place ■ People can't get to things	

Person-centred active support: A handbook

Problem	Comments
Not using people's methods of communication	
Negative or reactive approaches to challenging behaviour	
Staff doing for and to	

Appendix 3

The observation checklist

Service:... Date: ....

Name of person we support observed:...

Name of observer:...

Name of staff member(s) observed: ....

1. Environment
■ Was the environment comfortable? (Consider temperature, light, noise) ■ Is the location suitable? (Assess community facilities, open spaces) ■ Were there any notable issues regarding safety, crowding, music, presence of objects and materials, location of furniture, access to equipment, or other environmental conditions?

What makes sense? What works? What needs to be maintained?	What doesn't make sense? What needs to change? What doesn't work?

2. Routines and predictability	

- To what extent are the activities predictable for the person, with regard to what will be happening, when it will occur, with whom and for how long?
- Did the outcome of the observation match what was planned or expected by the person being supported?
- To what extent did the person have the opportunity to make choices about his or her activities and reinforcing events?
- Was the pace and level of activities or interactions matched to the person's likes and needs?

What makes sense? What works? What needs to be maintained?	**What doesn't make sense? What needs to change?** What doesn't work?

3. Interactions with staff, people we support and others	

- How many people were typically around the person? Does the person seem bothered in situations that were more crowded or noisy?
- Were there people the person particularly enjoyed or disliked interacting with?
- What was the pattern of staffing support the person received? Do you believe that the number of staff or their social interactions matched the person's needs and preferences?

What makes sense? What works? What needs to be maintained?	**What doesn't make sense? What needs to change?** What doesn't work?

4. Staff skills and confidence

- Were staff confident and comfortable in their approach and interactions with the person?
- What did the interactions tell you about staff's beliefs about the person?
- Did staff have the skills and confidence to support the person in activities or when behaviour is difficult or challenging?
- Was support provided in a way the person we support seemed comfortable with?
- Did staff provide appropriate levels of social interaction and assistance? (Not too little, not too much)

What makes sense? What works? What needs to be maintained?	**What doesn't make sense? What needs to change?** What doesn't work?

5. Communication

- Was speech (or alternative forms of communication) matched to the person's ability?
- Were signs, gestures and pictures used to back up speech?
- Were staff in a good position when communicating to the person? (e.g. the person could see and hear them clearly, gain the person's attention before starting)
- Did staff check that the person had understood what they were communicating?
- Were communication books and aids used consistently?
- Did staff observe and respond to all communicative signals?

What makes sense? What works? What needs to be maintained?	**What doesn't make sense? What needs to change?** What doesn't work?

6. Any other comments/suggestions

Appendix 4

The observation of engagement and the quality of staff support

Section 1: Observation recording sheet

Name of service			
Name of person observing and assessing			
Date of observation	DD	MM	YY
Start time		End time	
Number of people supported present		Their initials	
Number of staff present		Their initials	

Use the table below to record what the people supported and staff are doing. There is a continuation sheet if you need more space. You should put the initials beside entries to show who was doing what. Make sure you pay attention to what people are not doing as well as to what they are doing. At the end of the observation, thank those taking part and give constructive feedback.

Activity of the person being supported	Staff activity

Section 2: Rating of quality of staff support

	Rating	Notes for feedback to service – helpful hints and successful strategies
In general, people are engaged in meaningful activities and relationships, and therefore developing in independence, choice and social inclusion.		
Staff support people to participate in a range of real activities.		
Staff are observed to offer choices and respect decisions appropriately.		

	Rating	Notes for feedback to service – helpful hints and successful strategies
Staff are observed to present activities well.		
Staff are observed to prepare activities well.		
Staff are observed to provide graded assistance to support people to successfully participate in meaningful activities and relationships.		
Staff interact with people in a warm, positive and helpful style.		

Rating scale:

1 = Very weak (could do a much better job than this)

2 = Weak (inconsistent, poor performance, could be improved)

3 = Adequate

4 = Good (many strong points, consistent good performance)

5 = Excellent (outstanding, hard to do better than this)

Section 3: Summary of observation of activity within each service

Using the information gathered in section 1, rate each person's level of engagement, the choice offered and the nature and variety of the activities.

Person's initials	Engagement (in meaningful activity) Enter 1 – 5 in the box	Choice Enter 1 – 4 in the box	Variety of activities Enter the number of activities in the box	Describe the kind of activities observed
	☐	☐	☐	
	☐	☐	☐	
	☐	☐	☐	

Rating scale for engagement

1 = Extremely weak (was disengaged throughout)

2 = Very weak (only engaged in self-care activities e.g. eating or drinking)

3 = Weak (was involved in some small parts of activities, other than self-care activities, even though able to participate more fully – lots of opportunities for engagement missed)

4 = Good (was actively engaged in large sections of the task but some disengagement which was not explained by clear individual choice or preferences, established risk assessment)

5 = Very good (was actively engaged in a range of activities throughout the observation period apart from when the person clearly chose to stop an activity and rest, or where an established risk assessment or support assessment had dictated that a particular part of a task needed to be completed by staff)

Rating scale for choice

1 = Very weak (no real choice offered by staff to individuals and decisions made by people were not noticed)

2 = Weak (one or two choices offered but not in an accessible way for individuals, and decisions made by people were noticed but not respected)

3 = Good (one or two choices offered with appropriate support to make the choice, and decisions made by people were respected as much as it was feasible)

4 = Very good (a range of choices offered with appropriate support and decisions made by people were noticed and respected)

N/O – use this code if no opportunities for choice existed

Section 4: Practice leadership

Using your observations, informal conversations with people and a brief check of supervision and team meeting minutes, rate the service in terms of practice leadership.

Senior staff are providing practice leadership (spend time with every member of staff, give feedback and model good practice)	☐
Supervision happens frequently (as per Adepta policy) and focuses on quality of support provided by each member of staff	☐
Staff meetings happen frequently (as per Adepta policy) and focus on engagement of each individual supported	☐

1 = Very weak (could do a much better job than this)

2 = Weak (inconsistent, poor performance, could be improved)

3 = Adequate

4 = Good (many strong points, consistent good performance)

5 = Excellent (outstanding, hard to do better than this)

Further comments for improving practice

Signature of assessor...

Appendix 5

Observation of engagement and the quality of staff support: A guide

General information

This brief measure of engagement, quality of staff support and practice leadership, has been designed for use by operational managers and by members of the quality assurance teams. It is the formal recording of progress of each service, although it should be complemented by regular informal review of progress during monthly visits.

During these monthly visits, service managers should note what they see happening, such as how engaged people are and identify good practice to celebrate and any poor practice which needs to be targeted. These observations may happen more as a participant observer working with people living in or attending the service talk to people, or perhaps just while having a cup of tea with people.

The formal observations (e.g. every six months) need to be conducted with a little more discipline and it should be clear to staff that the managers are observing in order to avoid as many distractions as possible. Normally, you should observe for two hours but this could be broken down into two one-hour observation periods, if you think that this will provide more useful information. If it is broken down into two sessions, then you should complete one form for each period so that you can check to see if there are issues for particular individuals, particular staff or at different points in the day.

Each of the ratings should be completed at the end of the observation period in order to capture the full picture across the staff and the individuals being supported. While actually observing, managers should keep notes but concentrate on really taking everything in. Only rate what happened during the period of observation – make separate notes if you know about earlier activity (e.g. staff tell you that the people being supported chose the dinner menu) but do not include this in the ratings you make while you observe. This is your rating of what you observe and not of what staff tell you.

Observation details

Name of service			
Name of person observing and assessing			
Date of observation	DD	MM	YY
Start time		End time	
Number of people supported present		Their initials	
Number of staff present		Their initials	

Use the initial section to record the date, times, location of the observation plus the number of staff and people supported present during the observation. List the initials for those involved so you can check on changes for those people over time.

Section 1: Observation recording sheet

Activity of the person being supported	Staff activity

During the observation period, observers should record what the people being supported are doing and what staff are doing at the same time. Pay attention to whether staff are actually assisting people to do things and note the quality of the support provided. You should put the initials of those being supported beside entries in the first column. Make sure you pay attention to what people are not doing as well as what they are doing, i.e. watch for missed opportunities.

With regard to staff, pick up on good practice as well as areas of concern. In essence, you should be gathering the information that will help you complete the rest of the measure. You don't need to record what is happening minute by minute. You should write a brief account of what you see and hear continuously during the period. However, you might find it useful to record what is happening in five minute blocks so that you can look back and work out whether an individual was engaged or disengaged for most of the time etc.

Section 2: Rating of the quality of staff support

For each of the seven items on this part of the measure, rate the performance as follows.

1 = Very weak (could do a much better job than this)
2 = Weak (inconsistent, poor performance, could be improved)
3 = Acceptable (but could still improve)
4 = Good (many strong points, consistent good performance)
5 = Excellent (outstanding, hard to do better than this)

Examples of ratings are provided below, and these are based on the hands-on training checklist and the essentials of active support. Record your notes for feedback to the service in the space provided. Try to pick up a mixture of positive and constructive feedback points, although for some services there may initially be more 'helpful hints' than 'successful strategies'. Please note that these ratings are independent of any rating of individual level of ability – services can score a five even if the people they support have very severe and complex needs. If staff are providing good-quality support and people are engaged as much as they possibly could be engaged at that point in time, given their level of disability and complexity of needs, then that would be a score of five. In general, people are engaged in meaningful activities and relationships, and therefore developing in independence, choice and social inclusion.

Very weak

People are not engaged in activities other than eating, drinking or social activities. Alternatively, people might be engaged in one or two ad hoc and very simple activities (lower than their level of ability or experience) which involve a little staff support, such as carrying their plate into the kitchen after dinner and then going to sit down in the living room. You need to make some judgement here – in the early stages of implementing active support, simple activities might be the first steps but staff should be trying to involve people in smaller parts of more complex tasks such as meal preparation and gardening. And so overtime, scores should move up the scale even for the most severely disabled people.

Weak

People are engaged in a rather random fashion or with some people (those more able) engaged in activities while others are left disengaged. Lots of opportunities are missed to involve people although some are taken. Some staff do engage people, others don't.

Acceptable

Most opportunities to engage people are taken in the course of activities, all individuals are involved at least to some extent and all staff are involving people at least to some extent.

Good

All of the people supported are engaged in the main activities around the home or in the community, and staff are working as a team to support them consistently. Difference in engagement levels are due to the real choice and preferences of those supported and not to staff conceptions or preferences. Some opportunities might be missed to involve people in new and different activities, and staff might still do some things as staff activities – things that don't involve individuals being supported.

Excellent

All of the people supported are involved in all the activities of the home as much as is physically possible for them to be. Staff see ad hoc opportunities for involvement as well as planned activities (e.g. the windows need cleaning so they involve someone).

Staff support individuals to participate in a range of age appropriate real activities

Here you are looking to offer people adult activities which are not make-work. Weak practice would be staff giving someone a potato to hold and scrape with a table knife and then taking the potato and peeling it 'properly'. Good practice will include staff ensuring that they give enough assistance to make sure the task is complete at the time without the need to redo it later. Weak practice would also include things like washing people's 'twiddle' sticks or other items in a bowl of washing up instead of the dishes.

Age-inappropriate activities include using baby toys, activities involving play with dolls or soft toys, childish games (except where imitation is being used in intensive interaction, which would be social activity but not engagement in non-social activity).

Staff are observed to offer choices and respect decisions of the people being supported appropriately

Good practice here would be to see staff offering choices clearly, with appropriate communication methods for the person concerned and respecting the person's decisions. It would also be respecting reasonable choices people make in the course of an activity, e.g. which order to clean their bedroom, what order to serve the different elements of their dinner, when to stop etc.

Weak practice would be either offering no choice or very limited choice (i.e. between something and nothing) or offering choices in a way that would make it impossible for the person to understand, e.g. too many choices, inappropriate presentation, too verbal, no use of objects etc.

Staff are observed to present activities well

Good practice would include staff adapting a method of presentation appropriate to the communication needs of people, and even where they think the person understands verbal instructions or requests, usually accompanying this with objects helps people. Minimising distractions and using preparation to ensure that it is clear what the task or activity involves are also indications of good practice.

Weak practice could be only using a verbal presentation in another location of the house, with minimal or no preparation, or presenting a tasks in a way that isn't clear because of too much language or too much clutter in the immediate environment.

Staff are observed to prepare activities well

Good practice here would be indicated by staff adapting preparation to the ability of the person they are supporting. For the people who are able, preparation might be an important part of the task. However, for many people, having materials easily to hand to avoid waiting or having the activity interrupted is an essential part of good support. Staff should check that they have all the ingredients and equipment needed before introducing the task to someone, even when that person would take out the equipment, measure the ingredients etc. again. Other examples of good preparation would be evidence that staff have read through a recipe or practiced making something new before supporting someone to make it, or, for example, checking that the lawnmower works etc.

In contrast, weak practice would be a lack of preparation as described above so that the flow of the activity was interrupted or the activity didn't succeed. An example would be starting to bake and then finding there are no eggs; or going out to cut the grass and then finding someone had removed the blade of the lawnmower to have it sharpened; going out to wash the car to find that five minutes into the activity someone had to go to a doctor's appointment etc.

Staff are observed to provide graded assistance to support people to successfully participate in meaningful activities and relationships

Weak practice would be staff repeating the same level of support several times without success, or not providing enough support, perhaps providing too much support or the wrong type of support, e.g. hand-over-hand support when it is clear the person doesn't like physical touch.

Examples of good practice would be staff maximising the independence of people (letting them do as much as possible as independently as possible) but at the same time always ready to increase the level of help to ensure success. Examples of good assistance would be helping someone get into the right position to water plants and then letting go of the hose or the watering can for a few seconds, but carefully supporting as soon as the person's hand starts to drop; pulling forward cutlery in a drawer so that the person can reach more easily; holding the edge of something off the table so that someone can grasp it.

Staff interact with the people they are supporting in a warm, positive and helpful style

Here good practice would be illustrated by staff who have a warm rapport with people, but respectful at the same time. People are treated as adults and interactions seem adjusted to the preferences and needs of the individuals. Interactions are positive in style and encourage people to do things. Staff do not talk too much but just enough to help the person do the activities and then 'socialise' afterwards. This might depend a little on the individuals concerned, some might want to chat about things but talk should be dictated by the individual being supported not staff. Staff should respect the fact that colleagues are supporting an individual and should not interrupt unless in an emergency. Patient support, where staff give people time to respond is also a helpful style, and appropriate verbal praise is an example of positive interactions.

Examples of weak practice would be forceful interactions, such as telling people they 'have' to do something or that they must finish the whole task, or making people finish a task they had started, or telling someone to do a task 'properly', i.e. to the standards of staff. Language such as 'come on, do it, do it for me' is not helpful, nor is repeatedly calling someone's name until they eventually come. Forcing people to do things physically is also an example of weak practice, as is telling people not to do things, such as not to sit down, not to touch etc. Lack of respect can be seen in things like switching off or on the TV or radio, changing channels without asking, not allowing people to answer the front door etc.

Section 3: Summary of observation of activity

This section should be used to summarise what each of the individuals present were doing during the observation. Rate the engagement of each person as follows.

1 = Extremely weak (was disengaged throughout)
2 = Very weak (only engaged in self-care activities e.g. eating or drinking)

3 = Weak (was involved in some small parts of activities, other than self-care activities, even though able to participate more fully – lots of opportunities for engagement missed)

4 = Good (was actively engaged in large sections of the task but some disengagement which was not explained by clear individual choice or preferences, established risk assessment)

5 = Very good (was actively engaged in a range of activities throughout the observation period, apart from when the person being supported clearly chose to stop an activity and rest, or where an established risk assessment or support assessment had dictated that a particular part of a task needed to be completed by staff)

Rate the choice item as follows.

1 = Very weak (no real choice offered by staff to individual or decisions made by individuals were not noticed)

2 = Weak (one or two choices offered but not in an accessible way for individuals or decisions made by individuals were noticed but not respected)

3 = Good (one or two choices offered with appropriate support to make the choice or decisions made by individuals respected as much as was feasible)

4 = Very good (a range of choices offered with appropriate support or decisions made by individuals were noticed and respected)

Record 'N/O' if no opportunities for choice existed. It is unlikely that in a two hour observation there will be absolutely no opportunity for choice, however, sometimes if someone is engaged in one quite complex activity such as meal preparation, it is conceivable that the meal has to be prepared in a set way in order to ensure success and the choice of the person being supported is limited during the activity itself. In addition, choice over, for example, the menu for the evening might have been made earlier in the day and not observed.

In the space under 'variety of activities', record how many different activities the person was involved in and write down what these were, e.g. watching TV, peeling potatoes, talking to others, sleeping, etc.

You should use the notes sections on the back of the sheets to record any other information you think is worth noting. This should include things like the individual leaving half way through the observation to go shopping; whether access was gained to a community activity; if the person went to postural management for an hour, or slept in their chair for 45 minutes out of each hour.

Here, also note if people seemed to enjoy particular activities and if communication strategies of staff seemed to be working, and if additional adaptations or equipment would be useful for a particular person (e.g. a tray for his wheelchair). This section should allow you to give invaluable feedback to the service around particular individuals and help you over time to monitor whether all those supported by each service are getting the same level of opportunity for involvement, despite different levels of need.

Section 4: Practice leadership

This section will need to be completed using conversations with staff and by checking the team meeting and supervision minutes, as well as looking at the manager's observation checklists for staff, etc. Hopefully, you will see the manager having some input during the observations, but it won't be possible to rely on this for every service.

You need to check that the quality of staff support, both individually and as a team, and the engagement of those being supported, is a focus of team meetings and supervision. You don't have to slavishly read every single supervision minute but should sample a few every time for different members of staff (and also by different supervisors if seniors or deputies are responsible for supervision). With team meetings, you will be able to scan through the last five–six sets of minutes to check what is being discussed and hopefully you will have attended at least one meeting in the past six months.

Again you are asked to rate the three items on practice leadership on the following scale.

1 = Very weak (could do a much better job than this)
2 = Weak (inconsistent, poor performance, could be improved)
3 = Acceptable
4 = Good (many strong points, consistent good performance)
5 = Excellent (outstanding, hard to do better than this)

Some examples of how the rating might be applied are provided below.

Senior staff are providing practice leadership (spend time with every member of staff, give feedback and model good practice)

It is unlikely that this will be observed but house manager's observation forms should be available to sample, and supervision and team meeting minutes should show that feedback was given on performance. Staff themselves should report when asked, the last time the manager observed and gave them feedback.

Excellent practice would be when all staff spend time with the manager while working with individuals, and receive feedback and a model of good practice; also they are given regular supervision that focuses on engagement and active support. Regular team meetings would provide feedback on team performance in supporting activities, and senior support staff would also be providing good leadership and consistent supervision approaches etc.

Weak practice would be when there is no evidence of practice leadership and only some staff receive feedback on an ad hoc basis without a consistent approach. Perhaps senior staff are left to provide leadership when managers are still mostly in office, or there is little evidence of a focus on engagement, or supervision is not happening regularly and there is not a focus on staff performance in terms of active support. Staff may report that the manager is not present on the floor observing.

Supervision happens frequently (as per organisational policy) and focuses on quality of support provided by each member of staff

This is self-explanatory – check a sample of supervision minutes as illustrated above.

Staff meetings happen frequently (as per organisational policy) and focus on the engagement of each individual is served

This is self-explanatory. You should check minutes of meetings and if possible attend one staff meeting for each six monthly period. It would also be good to ask staff whether meetings were helpful to them to solve problems and to think through how to engage people more.

Appendix 6

Observation tips

Before

On arrival, make sure the people we support, the staff and others present know who you are and why you are there and tell them all that while observing, you will not be able to interact with them. Allow sufficient time for this before you start the observation, and make it clear to those present when you intend to start observing and start as close to that time as possible.

In order to help the people we support and staff to discriminate when they can and can't talk to you, make it clear at the outset of the session and put the observation checklist away when you have finished (it can also be useful to point out and use other visual clues, e.g. 'When I have my glasses on I'm "observing" so I won't be able to talk to you – when I take them off, I'm all done and you can talk to me again'). If you have been talking to the people we support or staff before the start of the observation, you should make it clear to everyone that you are going to start.

Once you have started the observation, further contact and attempts to interact or converse should be ignored. The people we support and staff will be less likely to initiate contact if you avoid eye contact as far as possible. This can all feel odd and a bit rude at first but it is the best way to get people to forget you are there, which means they will get on with what they normally do.

During

Walk into the room to a position where you can observe the person(s) being supported, avoid eye contact with anyone and stand as still as possible. Wear flat, soft-soled shoes that will not make a loud sound on stairs or hard floors. Close doors carefully. Do not handle materials, move objects or otherwise intervene in the environment, unless someone's safety is directly threatened.

Do not go into rooms where a person might reasonably be expected to be in bed asleep, undressed, or working with a member of staff on an activity which might be disrupted by other people coming in. Generally, this means not entering toilets, bathrooms or bedrooms at the beginning or end of the day. You should only enter these rooms if, for example, the person is doing housework.

After

Once you have finished observing, put away your checklist (or other visual cues) and tell everyone the observation has finished and spend some time socialising.

Before leaving, you should give feedback to the people we support and staff present (as long as it doesn't disrupt people's planned activities too much). This is important as it ensures people see observation as a positive experience and gives everyone present an opportunity to check out some of the things they may have liked to discuss or explain during the observation.

NB

Observing in the community can obviously be more difficult and is often more covert. It is advisable to take with you your ID and copies of a brief explanation of the purpose of the observation with contact details on it, so that it can be given to people who may approach you, such as a store manager.

Appendix 7

United Response 2009 Evaluation – Risk and benefit analysis

Risk/benefit analysis and participation information

It is anticipated that a number of people we support will have difficulties in giving or withholding consent to participate in the 2009 Evaluation project. However, because these are the very people who will benefit most from an independent observation of the support they receive, they should not be excluded from the evaluation without good reason.

If those who know the person well feel that they will have difficulty understanding the nature and purpose of the evaluation, and therefore make an informed choice about whether or not to participate, then the following procedure will be used. If it is felt that the person can understand the nature and purpose of the evaluation then an accessible consent form should be used.

Step 1: Risk/benefit analysis

The individual risk and benefit analysis will be completed to ensure that participation does not present any significant risk for the individual or other people who will be present during the observation. The attached form provides information on the general risks and benefits of the observation and should be used to record any other risk and benefits for the individual.

Where this risk and benefit analysis indicates that the risk to the individual or others is more than minimal, this will be recorded and the practice development team informed so that the observation can be cancelled.

Where there is no more than minimal risk, the observation will go ahead using the participation information below to ensure the person's wishes are taken into account throughout.

Step 2: Participation information

Whether or not a person we support is able to give their informed consent to participate in the observation, they will be able to demonstrate their thoughts and feelings about participating through their behaviour.

Observers are clear that an individual's willingness to participate will need to be assessed throughout the observation. If a person we support shows signs of being uncomfortable or upset by the observer's presence during the observation, this will be taken as evidence of withdrawal of agreement and the observation will stop immediately. In order to ensure observers are able to respond quickly, this section of the form should be used to describe how the person would let us know (verbally or non-verbally) that they did not wish to proceed or continue being observed.

United Response 2009 Evaluation

Risk/benefit analysis and participation information for: _____

Service: _____

Step 1: Risk and benefit analysis

Potential risk	Direct benefits
General Because daily routines and practices continue as normal throughout the observation, risk management procedures should have identified potential risks and risk reduction actions should have been taken. **Observers presence** The presence of an unfamiliar person in the house may become worrying or stressful for some people. Observers will minimise the effects of this by: 1. discussing suitable observation positions with the people we support and staff prior to the observation	**Direct benefits** An independent evaluation of the level and quality of support, which each person is receiving, provides an additional way for people's experience of being supported by United Response to be recognised and influence the support they receive. It provides an opportunity for people's non-verbal responses to support from staff to be recognised and communicated to staff. Feedback and discussion about the observation both with the individual and United Response staff promotes person-centred support. It recognises where things are working well, sparks ideas and identifies areas for development.

Potential risk	Indirect benefits
2. ensuring the people we support know of their right to withdraw from the observation at anytime, where ever possible 3. utilising 'withdrawal of consent indicators' provided as part of the pre-visit preparations throughout the observation. If a person we support expresses or displays signs of being unhappy or uncomfortable with the observer's presence, this will be taken as evidence of withdrawal of consent and the observation should be stopped immediately. **Invasion of privacy** Observers have been clearly instructed not to go into rooms where a person might reasonably be expected to be asleep in bed, undressed or engaged in an activity, which might be disturbed by another person coming in. Observers will not enter toilets, bathrooms or bedrooms without being invited by the person we support to do so. **Confidentiality** Observers are currently employed by United Response and the existing code of practice regarding confidentiality will apply. Initial feedback and service specific reports provided to area and service managers will be treated as private and confidential. No names or specific locations will be used in data analysis, publications and presentations.	**Service and staff** The information gained from the observation provides positive and constructive feedback to teams on the support they provide, which will be incorporated into individual and service planning discussions. Feedback from the observation, additional support and advice from the practice development team, which results from the observations, will assist services to continue to develop person-centred approaches. Information from the observation will be used in the development of appropriate training for staff at a local and national level to ensure staff becoming more skilled and confident in supporting people at home and in the community. **United Response** This evaluation provides the organisation with an objective assessment of the support United Response provides, which will inform national training strategies and corporate planning. It also enables United Response to monitor progress on the development of person-centred approaches as well as identify elements that contribute to successful implementation.
= No more than minimal risk and significant benefits for people being supported by United Response	

Individual risks and benefits	
For each person we support, the risks and benefits as well as the probability of harm will depend on the individual and their circumstances. For example, while for some people we support having someone new in the house will not cause any substantial risk or distress; for others, the presence of an additional person in their environment may cause considerable anxiety and lead to high levels of challenging behaviour. Using the space below, record any individual risks and benefits for the person if they participate in the observation.	
Risks	**Benefits**
Is the risk more than minimal? Is the probability and magnitude of harm or discomfort anticipated greater than those ordinarily encountered in everyday life?	

Person-centred active support: A handbook

Yes	No	
Record the decision below and return this form to the practice development team so that the observation can be cancelled.	Step 2: Participation information	
	Describe how the person would communicate (verbally or non-verbally) that they are uncomfortable or unhappy during observation and return this form to the practice development team.	
Name	Signed	Date